To good health
+
enner peace!

Janice Alpert

Books by Janice Alpert

I Always Start My Diet on Monday
The I-Quit-Smoking Diet

I Always Start My Diet on Monday

A Unique Program to Permanently
Conquer
Emotional Overeating

Janice Alpert, M.A., L.C.P.C.

Pearl Publishing
Northfield, Illinois

Library of Congress Catalog Card Number 96-071739

Back Cover Photograph by Fran Kapp
Editing, Cover and Text Design by Whitney Scott

ISBN 0-9655023-0-9

PRINTED IN THE UNITED STATES OF AMERICA

ACKNOWLEDGEMENTS

First and foremost, I thank my friends and family for their support and encouragement. Their unconditional faith has been invaluable. Next I thank the hundreds of clients who have shared their pains and triumphs; working with all of you has been a labor of love and learning. Thanks to Marla Heller, R.D., L.D. – a learned nutritionist who agrees that food is a pleasurable part of life – for understanding and writing an eating plan that is inclusive rather than exclusive and incorporates *all* foods. Finally, a *huge* thank you to my editor, Whitney Scott. Her time, patience and dedication to excellence cannot be measured.

CONTENTS

TEN REASONS YOU'LL *NEVER* START ANOTHER DIET ON MONDAY

- **DIETS DON'T WORK.** Even if you lose weight, you'll probably gain it back...and more.

- **DIETS COST $$$.** Instead of spending money on special foods, you can use that cash to pamper yourself.

- **DIETS ARE UNHEALTHY.** Severe dieting and yo-yoing can cause serious health problems.

- **DIETS ARE BORING.** Life offers many conversation topics far more interesting than fat grams and calories.

- **DIETS DON'T DEAL WITH FEELINGS.** Staying focused on food and weight keeps you from dealing with emotions and life.

- **DIETS REINFORCE DENIAL AND DEPRIVATION ISSUES.** A "Good Food"/"Bad Food" mentality persists when dieting. Food, ALL food, should be an enjoyable and pleasurable part of life. Food is not the enemy!

- **DIETS STEAL YOUR TIME.** Just think of the time and energy spent thinking and worrying about food, diet and weight. This reclaimed time can be used for far more meaningful life experiences.

- **DIETS ROB ENERGY.** Restrictive eating often deprives the body of necessary fuel – without fuel, energy ebbs.

- **DIETS CAN BECOME EATING DISORDERS.** The obsession to be thin and to succumb to society's norm of the body beautiful can lead to anorexia, bulimia, compulsive overeating and exercising extremes.

featuring...
The No. 1 Reason You'll Never Diet Again

- **DIETS NEVER BRING SELF LOVE AND INNER PEACE.** Focusing on self – not weight – creates self confidence, genuinely good health, and a sense of well-being and self-love integrated into your life forever.

Chapter One
About Myself: About Change

You *are browsing through the diet section* of your local bookstore, and the title of this book caught your eye. Or perhaps a friend who knows you well purchased this book for you as a gift. Either way, I can relate! For years, I, too, spent many an hour and dollar searching for the "perfect diet" book, or program that would free me of excess weight and mental anguish from repetitive dieting, subsequent weight gain, and constant dissatisfaction with myself and my appearance. I am pleased to share with you that this time, you have come to a good place to begin the challenging process of permanent change.

Let me begin by sharing a bit about myself. Professionally, I am a psychotherapist in the Chicago area. I have been in private practice since 1981. I see individuals, couples, and families and also conduct a wide variety of workshops and seminars. Although I work with an assortment of issues including depression, co-dependency, and low self-esteem, my field of expertise is eating disorders. For the purpose of this book, I define an eating disorder to include all who feel that food, weight, diets, and preoccupation with their appearance controls their life. I chose this area of expertise for a very personal reason. From 1975-1980, I had an eating disorder.

Back then, I did not know I had bulimia. Bulimia entails ingesting large amounts of food (though as the syndrome progresses, many purge even small amounts of food), and then ridding the body of said food as quickly as possible. Some people induce vomiting, some take laxatives or diuretics, some fast, and some do excessive exercise. During my eating disorder I practiced both fasting and doing excessive exercise. In addition, almost 24 hours a day, my thoughts were centered around my eating plan for the day and my weight, two very common characteristics of anyone suffering with an eating disorder. Let me back up a minute to give you some history. As you are reading about my background, I encourage you to be thinking about your own.

I am the middle of three children. I have a brother who is two years older and a sister five years my junior. During my childhood, my mother stayed home (most women of that era did), and my father worked to support us. My father was a tailor. At 35, he decided to return to college for his bachelor's degree. Upon receiving this degree, he attended and completed law school. He has been a practicing attorney since I was eleven years old. Education and achievement were highly valued in my family; and so was food.

There was never an occasion or family gathering where eating was not involved. My parents grew up during the depression; therefore, wasting food was forbidden. I had to finish everything on my plate, because people in far off countries were starving. I never understood how finishing every morsel on my plate was beneficial to those who were starving in Africa.

I received strong messages about food. I quickly learned that food was more than just a necessity for good health. Rather, it was a symbol of love and power. If I was a loving person, then I would eat what my mother prepared, with a smile on my face, cleaning my plate. Not finishing or smiling resulted in being labeled "bad," hence, forfeiting dessert. Food was used as a reward for behaving well. If I cleaned my room without being asked, a chocolate cupcake awaited me. On the contrary, if I misbehaved, my punishment might result in relinquishing the same treat.

I don't believe my mother meant to connotate food in such a manner; however, she was overweight, as was her mother. Food meant a great deal to her. This is what was communicated: FOOD HAS MORE THAN ONE FUNCTION! I came from a family of genetic and emotional eaters. It was a cultural value, where food was an integral part of the woman's role as a mother, wife, and hostess. Being raised in this kind of environment, one might expect an overweight child. This was not the case for myself. Instead, I went in the opposite direction.

As a child, food was not that important to me. I was a very picky eater, which of course, drove my mother crazy. I was thin, and to her this was a fate worse than death. I had the ability to stop when I was full, and I did!

I will label this type of person as a "true thin." This type of person is innately born with, and in touch with, the mechanism "full." No matter where they are or what they are served, when they are full, they stop eating. These "true thins" can attend a wedding reception, and may only eat a strawberry from the sweet table. It doesn't matter that there are cakes galore. In the height of my eating disorder, I prayed this phenomenon would infiltrate my soul. Being full had nothing to do with eating, nor did hunger. More about this later!

This ability to eat when I was hungry and stop when I was full lasted through my teenage years. My weight was always normal. I looked fine until I was pregnant with my first child.

This brings up an important point. Unlike myself, most of my clients have struggled with their weight much of their life. What is interesting to note is that extreme weight gain, even for lifelong dieters, often occurs during some form of life crisis. I define the word crisis to include all things that set one's life into disarray. This may include such exciting things as a move, a promotion, or giving birth. A crisis may also include unpleasant things such as divorce, illness, or death. In my case, it was the wonderful occasion of my son's arrival. If you're a parent, you can surely understand how a newborn can cause a certain amount of turmoil, although joyous. I had no idea, as do many new mothers, how deep the love and anxiety I would experience. It was this life change, and the intense feelings that emerged, that influenced the outbreak of my eating disorder.

Looking back, throughout my pregnancy, I probably had

I Always Start . . . .

very normal concerns about motherhood and parenting. However, instead of paying attention to these thoughts and feelings, I found myself absorbed with worrying about a much safer issue: how quickly I could lose my weight. I had a difficult time dealing with my round, pregnant, body. I so feared looking like my mother and grandmother. I would do anything to be thin again right after delivering my son. I was extremely lucky I had a wonderfully short labor and a smooth delivery. To make matters even better, within a very short time I was back down to my pre-delivery weight, and wearing my old jeans. The problem was, that was no longer good enough.

During my pregnancy, I had read that Jaclyn Smith, the actress, was 5'8" tall and weighed 115 pounds. I decided since I was 5'7" tall, I, too, should weigh 115 pounds. The fact that I had always weighed around 125 pounds did not matter. I had a new goal, to be thin, really thin...like Jaclyn. My odyssey into the painful world of weight/food obsession began. In retrospect, occupying myself with food and diets was the safest way for me (and others) to avoid the other issues in my life. Scary feelings about motherhood, my marriage, and my life were kept on the back burner. Instead of facing these feelings, I would talk about diets, a popular and socially acceptable topic.

My first weight loss program consisted of eating all the protein you desired. This included beef, chicken, fish and eggs, but no carbohydrates. I accepted this. Although I couldn't have breads and sweets, I made up for it by eating large quantities of protein. The problem was, when a compulsive eater is told they can have ALL they want, they will. I did! I gained five pounds on that diet. I proceeded from there to a variety of other diets. I then became an avid exerciser. No matter who called me, when they would ask me how I was, my immediate reply would entail a lengthy response, including my daily weight, every morsel I had ingested that day, and what forms of exercise I had finished.

My entire life revolved around my menu.

One of my clearest, most telling examples occurred one evening when I was out to dinner with a friend, Susan. The waiter arrived and began taking our order. Susan ordered a wonderful meal, with a fabulous sauce. I ordered plain, broiled fish, and a dry salad. While we were waiting for our meal to arrive, I felt hungry. I reached into my purse for a four ounce bag of cut up raw carrots, which I had earlier prepared. Four ounces of raw carrots was all that was allotted on that particular diet program.

Curious, Susan asked what was in the bag. Needless to say, I began a long explanation of my new diet program. I went on and on about the merits of the program, how wonderful the food was, and how healthy I felt. I also told her she should be on it. Susan wasn't overweight. I just felt that since I was dieting, everybody should. The only thing I could focus on was food, dieting, and my weight, again, all easier to address than my true inner self. I didn't care that my friends might not have been interested in my diet. I often wonder how anyone remained friends with me.

As I continued discussing my new diet, and the value of carrying around raw carrots, Susan politely asked if she could have one. I looked at her with alarm. I quickly explained how the diet was calorically and metabolically balanced. If I were to give her a carrot, I would probably not lose weight, but even more frightening, I might gain! You can imagine her puzzled expression. Later, I pulled out my diet dressing, diet bread, and diet margarine from my purse. I'm sure Susan thought I was over the edge. She was not far off.

This is how my life went. There were only certain restaurants I would frequent. I would often call ahead of time to see if the restaurant had something I felt safe eating – low in calories and fat content. I kept only certain foods in the house. I thought if they weren't there, I would be "good" and stay on my plan, though it really didn't matter what was in the house when this overwhelming urge to overeat hit. I would go downstairs and eat everything. I weighed myself several times a day. My mood was determined by what the scale read.

I constantly searched for the new, and final answer. The miracle cure for my weight problem. I even attended a non-residential New Age Center, where they were offering a week long fruit fast. The counselor went around and asked all participants why they were there. The answers centered around better health, cleansing of the body, and higher spiritual attunement. My answer was plain and simple. I WANTED TO LOSE TEN POUNDS, FAST! Once again, I was in the wrong place. By the third day, I had a hamburger, fries, and a milk shake.

During my five year search for the "magic diet," I gained over thirty pounds. I would lose some weight on my "diet," but would gain it back, and then some. All my fears of looking like the other women in my family were coming to fruition. I was scared. I wanted to stop this crazy eating and fasting; I wanted to be normal around food. I just didn't know how. How many more times was I going to eat my healthy dinner, only to later binge on crackers, cereal, cookies, chips, or one of my favorites, doughnuts? I realized my eating wasn't due to physical hunger or taste. After all, by the time you're on your sixth doughnut, you're not tasting, you're gobbling! I missed so many parties because I had nothing to wear, or felt embarrassed about my appearance. I was afraid I'd overindulge – again. How many times would I have to lie down and suck in to zip up my jeans, and find ridges up and down my thighs after taking them off? Moreover, how many more Mondays would there be with promises of weight loss, this time for sure, only to have Friday come along and find myself at the nearest bakery?

I knew there was something wrong other than my inability to stay on a diet. As a "walking-talking-caloric dictionary," a "self-taught nutritionist," and an "exercise aficionado," I should have been able to lose weight and keep it off – if that had been the extent of the problem.

As time passed, I came to terms with the fact that I might need psychological help. My gut was saying I needed a new direction. However, the thought of talking to someone about my innermost feelings scared me. Talking "diet" seemed safe, secure, and familiar. Talking about my deepest emotions didn't feel as safe, secure, and was absolutely unfamiliar.

The fear I was experiencing is quite common. Facing the unknown is always unsettling. Given a choice, most of us will stay in a familiar situation, even if it's painful, rather than seek the unknown. This customary condition becomes a safe haven. This is why many people don't divorce their abusive spouses, or quit their unsatisfying careers. People generally avoid risk. Therefore, we avoid change. The discomfort of a current situation has to become extreme before we are ready to move. For instance, in the 1992 presidential election, we were dissatisfied enough with Bush, that we were willing to bank on a new president, rather than stay with the known.

I finally reached the point where I was uneasy enough with my current condition, that I was ready to explore myself, my life, and yes, my eating. It occurred to me the day my good friend had a luncheon. Here is what happened.

Lynn and I were acquaintances in high school, and met again on vacation. We hit it off immediately. She had a great personality, a young child, and best of all, she was obsessed with her weight. We soon became diet partners. On Monday, of course, we would start our new diet. We made all kinds of rules. Prizes were even awarded to whomever stuck to the plan or lost the most weight. Sometimes, we would even put up money. We started with a dollar a cheat. If either of us went off the diet, we had to 'fess up, and give the other person a dollar. The problem was, a dollar wasn't that big a deterrent. When that urge for a brownie hit, a dollar extra seemed well worth it. We increased the amount to ten dollars a cheat. This made things a lot more interesting.

One day I was driving along and decided I wanted something sweet. Problem! I didn't want to pay Lynn ten dollars. While pondering this dilemma, I decided, if worse came to worse, I could always lie to Lynn. This seemed to be the perfect answer, except I couldn't do it. The more I thought about the fact that I was considering lying, I didn't know whether to laugh or cry. I satisfied my sweet tooth, and told Lynn the truth. Ironically, Lynn, too, cheated. The whole episode was a financial wash. We cheated ourselves, not each other.

Several years passed, and my friendship with Lynn grew to include areas of interest other than our weight. However, when either of us heard about a new weight loss program, we were sure to share it. The summer I finally decided to change, Lynn went on her own healthy weight loss/exercise program. To my dismay, she lost 20 pounds.

There was a part of me that was happy for her, but honestly, I was more jealous than happy. Lynn decided to throw a ladies' luncheon. I was positive that the main purpose of this gathering was to flaunt her new body. When I received the invitation, the first thing I thought of was, "Oh no! It's on a Wednesday!" It was one thing to go off my current diet on a weekend, but never in the middle of the week. I tried to calm myself down by realizing the party was still a few weeks away. I could still lose weight before the luncheon. My plan was to call Lynn ahead of time to ensure that I felt safe with the menu. She said she was serving chicken salad in a half of a pineapple, with some fresh muffins. At that point, I felt I could handle the afternoon.

The day of the luncheon arrived. I got there early to see if Lynn needed any help. She declined my offer, and offered me a drink. Lynn knew diet soda was my favorite thing to drink. When I asked Lynn for one she said, "Sorry, I am trying to eat healthy. That means no carbonated beverages. How about some fruit punch?" I got an ache in my stomach. I thought to myself, "Fruit punch is 80 calories a glass. Lynn knows I love diet soda, and she knows how crazy I get with empty, extra calories." I tried to get a hold of myself and remember I was an adult, and could survive an afternoon without a diet soda. I smiled and politely answered, "Fruit punch will be fine."

That afternoon I had not only the fruit punch, but everything in sight. I ate the muffins, the chicken salad, and the cookies Lynn served for dessert. I left Lynn's house and went to the nearest bakery, ice cream parlor, and 7-11. I ate all day and all night. Anything that I deprived myself of over the 5 years prior, I ate that day. By the time I got into bed, I looked like I was going to give birth. No baby was going to arrive. It was that very night when I was so physically and emotionally uncomfortable, that I decided I needed and wanted help. I wasn't going to another diet center. I was going to find a therapist.

If you, too, are at that point in your life where you're ready to examine yourself and your eating, you're in the right place. This book discusses what I learned, and also talks about what I now help others achieve.

In 1981 I lost my weight and learned a great deal about myself, life and food and am pleased to report this learning is ongoing. I have maintained my weight since 1981, eating a variety of foods, including the ones previously labeled "taboo" by most diet programs such as sweets and pizza.

• • •

If you're...ready to examine yourself and your eating, you're in the right place.

• • •

In the chapters that follow, I'll share how you, too, can permanently reach a reasonable body weight, and attain a healthier self-image. The mental fight with food will end. The number on the scale will no longer have such power. You will place a higher value on your character, rather than on your looks. Once you are more attuned to yourself, you will feel the demise of inappropriate food consumption and preoccupation with appearance. Instead you will experience a more satisfied and complete you.

Change and exploring the unknown can be scary. However, they can also bring a tremendous sense of gratification and peace. The following chapters will assist you in making these changes safely and comfortably. I'm sure you've heard stories of people persevering against incredible odds. For example, very poor people becoming millionaires, uneducated individuals finding a way to put themselves through school and becoming doctors, or the physically impaired challenging themselves to find success. How do these people make the changes needed to reach their goal? They succeed by working hard, being patient, and listening to their gut instincts.

Unfortunately, in American culture hard work and patience rarely receive the merit and value they deserve. In the United States, we are accustomed to the "quick fix." We want what we want, and we want it now. Whether it's watching television (my son rarely watches a program for more than thirty seconds without changing the channel), or seeing something at the mall that we think we need, even though it's not in our budget. Out comes the credit card. We disregard the reasons why we shouldn't do something so we can rationalize why we should do whatever it is we feel we want. Immediate gratification is what our culture promotes.

Hard work and patience are often labeled as dull and boring, rather than virtuous. How many women do you know who are continually attracted to the charismatic jerk who is fast and showy, rather than the nice guy? This need to have it all now is transferrable to our eating. In the short run, it does feel "good" to eat in abundance and not worry about the consequences. In the long run, as with our unnecessary purchase and our jerk mate, we feel both physically, emotionally, and even financially drained. To interrupt this disruptive cycle takes both time and patience. Waiting and hard work may feel tiresome at times, like studying for a final exam. Just as you feel rewarded when you receive a good grade, so it is with life's changes. The final result feels fabulous.

In addition to hard work and patience, another crucial ingredient to foster change is listening to your gut instinct. We all have our own gut instincts. These feelings are usually felt in our stomachs - hence, the term "gut instinct." If experienced and followed, they act as friendly guides. This can steer us in positive directions, keeping us out of harm's way. Most of us have had numerous life experiences where a tough decision needed to be made. Often, our head pushes us one way, yet we get a nagging pull from our insides that yells, "No, hold on!" If we wait and listen to this feeling, the result is affirming. On the unfortunate occasions when we ignore this wise voice, we usually pay the price.

There is a lot written on this feeling. Some people feel it is our "higher-self" guiding us. Others feel it is God's way of communicating. I don't have the definitive ruling on how gut instincts work; I just know they do. It's that feeling that brought you to this book rather than another gimmick diet program. Staying attuned to your gut feelings is a sure way to solidify the process of change with a sense of trusting calm rather than fear.

As you read this book, I encourage you to work hard, be patient, and stay in touch with your inner self. I believe all people have unlimited power and potential. There is no doubt that you can make the permanent changes you desire. The key word here is YOU. Often, clients come in and share success stories on various diets - comments such as, "The last diet I was on was wonderful. It really worked for me!" I quickly interject, "The 'diet' didn't work, you worked. The 'diet' stopped working when you stopped following it." There was no "magic" diet. If you eat fewer calories and expend more calories, your weight will drop. There is no magic; eat less, exercise more. That's how all weight loss occurs. The question is deeper: Why don't we all do it?

• • •
All people have unlimited power and potential.
• • •

The possibility for success does not lie in some new Shangri-la. Success lies where it should, inside YOU. Do not shy away from accomplishing your goals and reaching future aspirations. I wrote this book for all who ingest its material, to ease the changing process. I want to help make this process as comfortable and peaceful as possible. The following chapters are filled with information giving you the foundation to change. The rest is up to you to build from there.

Chapter Two
Food Is Not the Enemy

As *you begin this process of change,* the first step is to address your relationship with food. As the title of this chapter suggests, it's crucial that you learn and understand that food is not the enemy. The idea that food is not "BAD" will be a new notion for many chronic dieters, those suffering from bulimia or anorexia, and compulsive eaters. Engaging in countless "diet" programs has led many people to learn endless rules about what foods are "okay" to eat, and what foods are not.

The foods that are labeled "okay," "legal," or "safe," usually include fruits, vegetables, grains, low fat cottage cheese, skim milk, fish, skinless chicken, just to mention a few! Foods considered "not okay," "illegal," or "unsafe," include sugars, chips, ice cream, pizza, or any kind of red meat. The problem with these rules is simple: in their absolute form, over the long term, they do not work.

Before all the nutritionists, doctors, and vegetarians get all up in arms, let me explain. I have nothing against people who choose to eat in the above manner. Certainly, you would have to be living on another planet not to be aware of the advantages of eating healthy food, and avoiding foods high in fat content. However, my experience with people who have suffered from weight issues leads me to believe they would do better in the long run with more variety in their meals and snacks. Most people who struggle with their weight really enjoy the taste, texture, and smell of food, ALL FOOD. Their palette is usually very sensitive to taste. Unfortunately, this sensitivity to the pleasures of food has been ostracized by our culture. People have been made to feel that enjoying food is a flaw in one's character we must continually overcome. This notion must be challenged.

Whatever rules about food you have been living with must

I Always Start . . . .

be altered. Again, it's fine to be concerned with health issues including blood pressure, cholesterol and heart disease. Those who have gone on weight loss programs filled with strict rules which involve eating only fruits, vegetables, and lean protein, know only too well – they may experience some weight loss. But soon after, they may gain the original pounds back, plus additional weight. This "yo-yo" pattern has proven to be an extremely unhealthy way to live. A solution that usually works better is learning to eat all the foods we love, in moderation. In order to lose weight and keep it off, discontinuing this "yo-yo" cycle is necessary. As mentioned, it has often been noted that people who follow these extremely restrictive plans inevitably gain back whatever weight they may have lost, and then some! The method I'm going to suggest will offer a slower weight loss, but will be permanent.

During my eating disorder, one of my primary goals was for food to not really matter to me. I never wanted to think about my meals, how I was going to handle parties, or what snack I could feel safe eating. I wanted to only eat when I was hungry, stop when I was full, and only use food as a fuel for my body. These ideas had been drummed into my head by every diet program, as to the way I "should" be handling food. I bought their package. The problem was, food was (and is) important to me. I love(d) the taste of food, and ironically, the only time this love was not present was when I was eating in an uncontrollable manner. More about out of control eating later.

Most of us don't use food solely for energy. Rather, food is eaten for pleasure. During my struggles with my weight, I tried diligently to de-emphasize the importance of food. The more I tried to ignore my enjoyment of food, the more important it became. To make matters worse, I compared my relationship with food to everyone else's! I had several friends who really didn't care about food. They enjoyed it, but it was not the end-all and be-all of their day, as it was for me.

One particular friend would frequently go all day without

eating. At around 4:00 p.m., she would suddenly realize she'd forgotten to eat lunch. I never understood that, and thought she walked on water. I wished I, too, could have forgotten about lunch and dinner.

Unfortunately, the more I tried to be like her, the earlier I ate my lunch. I finally realized I could never be like her. She never had a weight problem, so food was never an issue. It wasn't that she was stronger or better than I, food just didn't matter to her. This is a very important concept to comprehend. Placing naturally thin people who have never had a weight problem on a pedestal is ridiculous. They do not work at not using food inappropriately. Like the painter who paints without a lesson, or the born athlete who plays and wins from child hood on, these talents are inborn.

The same is true with people who are innately thin. Coming to the realization that I could not be like my friend was, in some ways, upsetting, but in other ways, it was freeing. I was upset because I felt if I could be like her, then my weight problems would cease forever. I felt frustrated knowing this would never happen to me. On the other hand, I felt liberated, as I could finally admit and accept that I DO LOVE FOOD, which does not make me, or you, a bad, weak, or inadequate person. You don't have to stop enjoying food to conquer a weight problem. On the contrary, the more you accept that you do enjoy, the quicker you'll see progress.

It is unrealistic to think that someone who has loved food all their life, can simply forget this pleasure. If an avid tennis player was told he could never wear his favorite brand of tennis shoes, each time he passed a shoe store, he, more than likely, would be wistfully looking at his favorite shoes. Even if another brand of shoes were just fine, his desire for his favorite would persist.

Human beings do not like being deprived or denied of any desired commodity...and as mentioned, this is certainly true in today's culture. There are times when we all need to set limits on our wants and needs. If we are emotionally healthy and mature, most of us understand and know that sometimes it is difficult to say no, yet we do find a way to do without something until we are able to attain what we desire. However, with food, we are told and believe that we can NEVER have what we love and enjoy. Never is a scary concept. It's unsettling to think that if the result of EVER eating cookies, chips, pastries or burgers is feeling fat or awful. I agree that if a person ate the aforementioned in one sitting for seven consecutive days, they would probably gain weight. Feelings of self-hate could also result. But if these food items are eaten in reasonable portions, a person can maintain their weight, or perhaps, even lose weight.

Eating in moderation is exactly how I lost, and have kept my weight off since 1981. The word diet suggests one is going "on" a new program. Common sense suggests that soon after, you will be going "off" the program. When "on" a new diet, one's eating is perfect. By perfect I mean no butter, sugar, salt or fat passes the lips. Eight glasses of water are regimentally swallowed a day. We are not enjoying ourselves! Soon we crave our favorite foods. We decide to just "taste" a cookie. After eating a cookie, we feel awful. We feel bad. We know we have blown it and say, "What the heck?" We then begin to eat everything we've deprived ourselves of, promising that tomorrow we'll be "good," and diet. This back and forth leads us to feel physically bloated and emotionally drained. It is this pattern that needs to be permanently arrested.

The eating pattern I've just described is also influenced by our emotional state of mind, a factor explored in the following chapters. Right now, I want to offer you a new guideline for food that will work for the rest of your life. Of course our bodies need food to live. Our mouths also need food for pleasure. Stop berating yourself for enjoying food. There is absolutely nothing wrong with deriving pleasure from the process of eating. When we eat properly, our pleasure is heightened. You need to get enjoyment from eating. Ironically, when someone breaks a diet by eating something "bad," pleasure is not part of the experience. Eating the first of ten doughnuts may be tasty; however, the tenth feels as though you're eating cardboard. What keeps us eating, even when taste is not a factor, is two-fold: One is a feeling of being deprived combined with "I blew it again, so I might as well eat everything today, because tomorrow I will be 'good' and start again," and the other issue which will be discussed more in the following chapters, is dealing with previously unnoticed emotions.

My approach allows you to eat a variety of foods. This assortment is not just allotted for the time you're on "this plan," but, throughout your life. When you can eat a cookie each day, it becomes less exciting, exotic, and untouchable. The more frequently you allow yourself to eat potato chips with your lunch, the less you'll crave them, and the less you'll gulp down an entire bag. As with any new eating plan, it's always wise to check with your doctor; next, here is what I suggest.

> • Each day you are to eat three meals and two snacks. There are two main stipulations. One, the foods you choose must be among your favorites. Two, you must watch your portions.

If this seems fairly simple, it is. Most of us feel dieting is a tremendous burden. Though I do feel you need to pay attention to what you're eating, especially the amounts, I don't feel you need to be overly concerned with what you're consuming. With my plan there is nothing, *nothing* you cannot have. The key is portion control. If you're not sure what a normal portion is, check the appendix in the back of this book.

A beginning guideline is to eat whatever you're eating now, but cut every portion in half. For example, if for breakfast you're having two waffles, and a large glass of orange juice, you might want to have one waffle and a small glass of orange juice. If for lunch you eat a large sandwich, an order of fries, and three chocolate chip cookies, I would recommend a half a sandwich, half the order of fries, and one cookie. You might be thinking that if the food is on your plate, then you know you'll finish it. My reply would be to get it off your plate, even if it means sending it back with the waiter or discarding it.

It's very important to accept that you're very vulnerable around food. This does not make you a bad person, just a bit shaky around food. Sending the food back or throwing it away is an important step in this process of changing your habits. You will not always need to remove the food, but for now you do. The important point here is that you want to start a new, healthier, more trusting, relationship with food. This takes time and patience. To experience eating a variety of foods that were previously considered taboo may feel both exciting and freeing, as well as a bit frightening. Your fear is understandable. You may feel you don't trust yourself to stop after one cookie. But you'll begin relearning and challenging your old rules about eating and stop after only one. Since you'll be able to put the brakes on with one and not desire the rest, you'll no longer feel bad about yourself. You'll feel less scared and finally begin to trust yourself and your body's ability to metabolize appropriately.

• • •

It's very important to accept that you're very vulnerable around food. This does not make you a bad person, just a bit shaky around food.

• • •

For your snacks, you may eat anything you wish, ranging

from 75-100 calories. Men may go to 150 calories. I usually recommend an afternoon snack between 3:30-4:00 p.m., and an evening snack around 9:00 p.m. This can include a piece of fruit or two Oreo cookies. I certainly don't want any nutritionists collapsing when I offer cookies as a viable choice for a snack. Fruit is fine, if that's what you want. But having a sweet regularly is physically and emotionally more healthy than depriving yourself of sweets for a given period of time followed by bursts of gorging. The goal is to build a healthy, normal relationship with ALL food.

You may be thinking you can't really lose weight while eating everything. This is not true. Many chronic dieters don't eat normally for a consistent period of time. They're either dieting or bingeing. They do not trust their bodies' abilities to metabolize a variety of foods. Due to crazy diets, they have altered their bodies' metabolic rates.

Assuming your thyroid is normal, your body should be able to digest and burn the new foods you are eating normally. Remember, with this plan, you're eating half of your normal intake. If you are eating less, weight should come off. Part of this plan means being patient. My way is not a gimmick or a quick fix. You want to be able to trust food, your body's ability to metabolize, and most importantly, yourself.

Another common concern is the issue of physical hunger. Many people do not yet have the ability to know when they're hungry or when they're full. Often, this is the result of being on several diets where extreme hunger for long periods of time was experienced. This hunger was then followed by binge eating, leading to extreme feelings of fullness. The in-between feelings of being hungry and then feeling satisfactory full are elusive. On this program, you should be able to experience normal hunger and satiation. Since many people are used to eating large portions, cutting back may feel like too little. Most of us do not, physically, need the amounts of food we eat. Our desire for huge portions may be more attributed to years of denial and mentally large appetites, than true physical need.

I Always Start . . . .

The two snacks in my program should preclude any major hunger pangs. This is not to say that you may not feel hungry during the course of an average day. That is normal. I usually eat breakfast around 8:00 a.m. By 10:30 or 11:00 a.m. I start to think about lunch, which I love! Since my lunch is always good and satisfying, it's not a problem to wait. When I was on very restrictive diets, I remember almost always feeling hungry and unsatisfied. It's not uncommon for chronic dieters to feel panicked when they first experienced a few hunger pains. Fear not! As you get hungry and satisfy yourself with delicious foods, you soon begin experiencing hunger as a normal physical sensation.

● ● ●

You want to be able to trust food, your body's ability to metabolize, and most importantly, yourself.

● ● ●

There is a difference between physical hunger and what I call "mouth hunger." Physical hunger is pretty self explanatory. You have not eaten in a while and your body tells you that it needs to be fed. Usually your stomach growls, and you know it's time to eat. Mouth hunger is different. This has more to do with a craving for something in our taste buds. This is fine. There is nothing wrong with wanting something just for the taste. My only guideline is to watch how much of it you consume.

This reminds me of a client I had several years ago. She was a successful, married businesswoman with three children, all under ten years old. She owned her own company with several employees. As she entered my office for her first appointment, I could not help but notice how impeccably she was dressed. Her clothes were color coordinated. Her accessories were carefully chosen, and her nails were beautifully manicured. It was my assessment that her appearance was important to her, and I was correct.

She began the session by sharing her desire to shed seventy-five pounds, and how important her appearance was to her personally and professionally. But she loved chocolate, especially Hershey chocolate kisses. She did not want to give up her favorite treat. She had heard about my weight loss philosophy which included eating all foods. She hoped that this approach would allow for chocolate. I assured her that it did.

I began taking her history. It wasn't long before that we focused on her current eating habits. She shared with me that each morning after getting the kids off to school, she would stop at the nearest 7-11 to buy a cup of coffee and a bag of Hershey chocolate kisses. She went on to say that this was her favorite breakfast. She loved to drink her coffee in the car, and to pop those silver bells into her mouth.

She made it clear she had no desire to give up her candy. I told her she didn't have to, but, there would be one change. Upon completing her purchase, and before leaving the store, she would have to throw away half of the bag of candy at the nearest garbage can. Instead of ingesting the entire bag (approximately 25 pieces of candy) she would only eat half. Her initial reaction to my suggestion was mixed. She was pleased that I wasn't going to "deprive" her of her chocolate. However she wasn't too happy with being able to eat only half of her normal amount, not to mention the issue of being wasteful.

Being wasteful is a big issue for many people. My response to this is to remember that eating all that extra food turns into fat in our bodies. Extra fat is also a waste – a waste that has many more unhealthy variables than throwing the food away. Although I am not a waste advocate, I am an advocate for good health, and physical and emotional well-being. At this point, discarding some food is the better, healthier choice. If you feel terrible about all the people that are starving in this world, I would recommend sending a donation to your favorite charity. In contrast to overeating, this would be a very helpful, healthy alternative. Remember that discarding extra food, and eating only half portions in a restaurant is a temporary intervention. Ultimately, the safer you feel with different foods, and the more trust you feel within yourself, the easier it will be to bake, or keep sweets in your house. Part of learning to be normal and healthy around food, is to understand that right now you can't handle certain kinds, and quantities of food. Be patient.

Back to my client. Although skeptical, she agreed to try my plan for one week. To minimize her feelings of denial from eating only half the amount, I told her that if she really felt that she needed more, she could always buy more at work. Each morning she went into the 7-11 store and purchased her coffee and Hershey kisses. Before she left the store, half the bag of candy went into the garbage. This was very difficult for her. She wanted to be able to save the extra half for the next day. However, she remembered that, right now, she didn't have enough inner strength to save the other half for the following day. The likelihood of not eating the remaining candy before the day ended was very slim.

After one week, she lost two pounds. She was also eating her regular lunch, dinner, and two snacks. After four weeks, she lost eight pounds. She could not believe what was happening. What was even more surprising and pleasing to her was that after the first month, she began craving cereal for breakfast. The more permission she was given to eat chocolate, the less she seemed to need it. This is not to say that she didn't have any. However, the sense of urgency subsided greatly. Learning that chocolate is not the enemy, and confronting other issues in her life, she shed over fifty pounds. She found that she was quite content with her new body and the variety of wonderful foods she now could enjoy. The remaining twenty-five pounds that she wanted to lose became less of an issue. She was happy with herself.

The main point is to set up a program that includes all the foods you truly enjoy, and eat them regularly. For those who are thinking, "I don't know if I can trust myself to eat just one cookie right now. I'm afraid that if I eat one I will eat twenty!" For now, do not include cookies in your program. The foods that are the scariest for you – the ones you fear you will binge on – need to be added to your eating plan gradually and safely. Remember, it will not be this way forever!

For example, when I first began including new foods, I intentionally excluded doughnuts. I was sure from my previous behavior that if I ate one, I would not be able to stop. I did not feel I could control myself around doughnuts. I began by choosing foods that, although I considered "bad," or "fattening," I once was able to eat in a controlled, limited quantity. For instance, on one of my previous diet programs, I was allowed a two ounce serving of ice cream, or one chocolate chip cookie each day. As I followed this program to the letter, I did lose weight while enjoying these "forbidden" foods.

Since I wasn't sure I could handle these pleasurable foods in my home yet, I'd get in my car each day and drive to the nearest ice cream parlor or bakery to purchase one of the allotted items. I'd eat it as soon as I left the store with a smile on my face. I was so happy I could have a treat and not feel guilty, or feel like I was a bad person. There were times when I asked the ice cream, or bakery clerk to weigh or measure a certain item. I felt silly and embarrassed, feeling I "should" be able to handle sweets on my own, and in an adult manner. At the time, however, I could not.

You must accept your vulnerabilities and grow from there. Understanding that it's difficult to deal with food non-judgmentally, is a crucial step for the journey to safe, relaxed visits to any grocery store, restaurant, bakery, party, and your home. I am happy to share that I can easily go to any grocery store, restaurant, bakery, party, or stay at home with a variety of previously scary, taboo foods, without feeling obsessed or uncertain. Ultimately, you can as well.

This will take time. Be patient and honest with yourself. When you're eating a new food such as a sweet or something salty, continually talk to yourself with warmth and encouragement. Say "What I'm eating is fine. I haven't blown anything and I'm not cheating. Loving this cookie or chip doesn't make me a weak person. I'll still lose weight. I am so proud of myself that I'm learning to eat a variety of foods. I am so pleased that, at last, I'm building a new relationship with food and myself." Having these rational talks is so important. Much reevaluation needs to take place when you're creating this new eating experience.

Also important in this transformation is trying to stay in touch with the physical sensations of hunger and fullness. As previously mentioned, this is very difficult for many chronic dieters. Most are not attuned to feeling full. This disconnection is why it's almost impossible for individuals to stick to programs or self-help books that encourage eating what you like, and then stopping when full. Although I do agree with this approach in theory, the reality is it's not applicable to most who suffer with weight/eating issues. Usually, chronic dieters are either starving on some new diet, or stuffing themselves on marathon eating escapades. As already mentioned, they're not familiar with the interim process of feeling physically hungry, eating, and stopping when full. This process needs to be relearned.

Eating three meals and two snacks virtually guarantees that you will be neither "starving" nor "stuffed." You should feel a bit hungry, then comfortably satisfied. I want you attuned to how hunger feels, and how good it feels to be comfortably full, not stuffed. This may take some planning on your part. Anything else in your life that you want requires expending a certain degree of effort, as with creating a new relationship with food. Accepting that food is important to you should encourage you to plan your meals and snacks.

• • •

Usually, chronic dieters are either starving on some new diet, or stuffing themselves on marathon eating escapades.

• • •

This planning is very important in achieving success. So many of my clients feel that planning their meals is very reminiscent of past diets. The result is that they resent putting in the time and energy involved. My response is to remind them, and you, that this time it's different.

Such planning does not have to be done in an obsessive, compulsive, and absolutely restrictive manner. Rather, it should be done in a self-loving, caring way. We need to cater to our needs, just as we would care for the special needs of a sick child. Our bodies need fuel, and our taste buds need stimulation and satisfaction. The more you take care of your physical needs and tactical taste needs for food, the easier it will be to address the other emotional reasons which cause you to overeat.

Planning is also a preventive intervention that will lower the chances of just grabbing for anything. Grabbing often leads to unhealthy bingeing. This is a lifelong commitment to caring for yourself. Treat yourself like you would a best friend.

When you include a variety of foods in your everyday life including parties, restaurants, and at home, feelings of resentment, denial, and deprivation diminish. When you are eating three meals a day and two snacks, your body's need for fuel is honored, and your taste buds are pleased. On the occasion that an overwhelming desire to over-indulge strikes, it will become evident that there must be something else

I Always Start . . . .

occurring.

In the pages that follow, I will be addressing what these other factors include, and how to understand and resolve them. We will begin to see how eating has been used as a pain killer for our suppressed emotions. The first priority, for now, is to make sure that you're eating three meals and two snacks that you enjoy. Again, your main guidelines are to watch your portions, pick foods that you love, and try to plan ahead. The more you do this, whether at a restaurant or at a buffet, the easier it will be to send half of your meal back, or not go back for more. You will feel much better about yourself.

However, remember that dieting and overeating is something you have done for years. In many ways, it does feel comfortable. It is what you know. Watching and taking care of yourself – physically and emotionally – and learning to eat a variety of new and delicious foods is new and unusual. When you do something new, be aware that you might feel a little uncomfortable. But fear not! Soon these feelings of awkwardness dissipate. Remember that first time you drove, and applied pressure to the breaks. I don't know about you, but my dad and I almost went through the window. Learning to feel comfortable with eating a wide variety of foods, knowing when you're hungry, and stopping when you're full takes time and practice.

Begin eating those three meals and two snacks, and enjoy. Watch your portions, and always remember there's no such thing as a "wrong" food, just inappropriate amounts. I want to reiterate that this also includes fats. There has been so much written about avoiding fats that many weight loss programs prohibit any ingestion of them. Many of my clients follow, or try to follow, this advice. The fear that swallowing one teaspoon of butter or salad dressing will cause an immediate weight gain keeps people away from these foods. I am certainly not recommending that you should grease your bread with butter, and douse your salad with a half a cup of salad dressing. However, I am saying use common sense. A little fat in your program, if you enjoy it, will not prevent you from losing weight. You can have regular salad dressing, if you choose. Excess weight is generally not there because someone used a tablespoon of regular salad dressing on their salad!

Remember, food is not the enemy, and you are trying to challenge many of the old diet rules. Being able to incorporate all foods into your eating plan, and finding out that your body will metabolize them appropriately, can only be accomplished through experience. You need to find out what foods are best for you.

This reminds me of a speech that I gave several years ago. I spoke for an hour, sharing with the audience my views about eating a variety of foods - all foods. I also discussed what you'll be reading in the following pages - the emotional reasons we overeat. During the question and answer portion of the program, one woman rose and was quite indignant. She had recently attended a spa, where all the food was fat free, sugar free and salt free (YUK!). She went on to expound on the health benefits of this type of eating. How dare I suggest that it's perfectly okay to include sweets, chips, and cookies in their eating plan? My response was clear. "I have nothing against choosing a specific lifestyle eating plan that is geared toward specific food, if an individual prefers. But the key word here is choice." Most of the people that I have dealt with I don't believe really had a choice. They have felt awful about themselves, they have felt weak and inadequate about their weight, and their inability to eat "correctly." This is what I feel is imperative to change. I want you to be able to choose your own lifestyle eating plan based on you needs. This would include your history around food and weight, your taste requirements, and your health.

I do have one other recommendation for those who are still confused about what a reasonable portion might look like, or feel they need some additional structure in designing their eating plan (other than what I offer in Appendix 1). Feel free to consult a local nutritionist who is familiar with an exchange program. With an exchange program, although structured, you still have a great deal of freedom in choice. A large variety of foods is available. Seeing a nutritionist can also be helpful if you have any health problems that need monitoring or you just need somewhere to check in.

Whatever you decide, remember that you need to be able to live with your choices daily. Do what feels comfortable for you. If you are uncertain whether or not you are getting all the required nutrients, contact your physician.

In conclusion, don't forget: FOOD IS NOT THE ENEMY! From this point on, I will be addressing other underlying issues that cause a seemingly intelligent, sane, human being to repeatedly eat in an out-of-control manner. As you will see, it's rarely about the food.

Chapter Three

Feelings Are Why We Overeat

 Now *that you are eating* three meals and two snacks that you are truly enjoying, it's time to explore the emotional reasons you inappropriately turn to and use food. On those awful days when you have eaten in an out-of-control manner, it is not attributable to some random phenomenon. It's not a twist of fate that on some days you can eat fairly normally, and on others you feel compelled to ingest everything in sight. It's not some force from above that suddenly overcomes you and compels you to open the refrigerator, hoping something new and wonderful will appear since you last opened it an hour before. Nor does your bakery lack tasty things on Monday, but have them on Friday, when you must buy everything. What drives people to use food in a self-abusing manner are feelings.

Every day, I listen to people who share feelings of imprisonment by a powerful preoccupation with food, diets, and their weight.

> *"My weight is all I ever think about. At restaurants I am always worried about what I can feel safe ordering. The worst part is when I do order properly, I then go home and overeat crackers and chips! I cannot help but wonder what is wrong with me. Why do I keep doing this?"*

> *"My very first thought each morning is whether or not I can eat like a normal person today."*

> *"Just knowing that I will start my diet tomorrow is reason enough to permit myself to eat anything and everything today!"*

I Always Start . . . .

All of these clients are well aware that these uncontrollable desires for food are not really related to the actual food item. They know what is appropriate to eat. After all, many of them label themselves "professional dieters."

They can eloquently debate the merits of any past diet program, and give a fairly accurate review of all the current ones. They can even recite, from memory, the caloric content of everything from a Big Mac to four ounces of chopped celery. Even though they, like myself, are "walking-talking caloric dictionaries," "self-taught nutritionists," and "exercise/fitness experts," the powerful urge to eat always returns. This awful impulse is the forerunner to extra pounds and, even more harmful, to feelings of self-defeat, and self-hate.

Sandy, one of my clients, freely admits that her preoccupation with thinking and worrying about food and weight was driving her crazy. She is a busy mother of two, and works as a part time travel agent. She has a lot of friends and a nice family. However, her weight was always on her mind. This obsession heightened whenever she began a new "diet." No matter how hard she tried to remain on her new program, nightfall would arrive, and she would find herself prey to the midnight binge.

She confided, "After being good all day, in the back of my mind, I think about how fun a treat would be. I tell myself that I can't. I have to be good and stay on my diet. I know that eating a sweet will make me feel awful. I fight this thought throughout my day. However, the urge is too strong. It's all encompassing. All of my promises go right out the window. I just want to eat, NOW! I don't even keep anything that good in the house, hoping that will help. When the urge persists, and I have checked out the empty pantry, I simply throw on my coat, and speed off to the nearest 24-hour grocery store. I purchase only what I can hold. I do this shopping quickly, and with urgency. Before even leaving the store, the packages are voraciously ripped open. I eat rapidly, with little thought and certainly little enjoyment. As I pull up to my driveway, with sticky hands and feeling stuffed, I am filled with self-hate and disgust. I wish to never do this again, wondering why I did it in the first place. The entire episode is terrible, and I promise that tomorrow it will be different. However, it usually isn't."

Sandy's pain is evident, and she is not alone.

Merle is a 52-year old woman who lives alone. She works as a writer. She described her involvement with food, dieting, and her weight in this way, "I feel as though I have a terminal disease called 'food on the brain.' I think about food and what I weigh throughout my day. Each day is an internal struggle to pass the vending machine at work without inserting two quarters. My whole life revolves around food and eating; I go around and around, and go nowhere. I dread holidays, parties, restaurants, and staying home. Although others see me as competent and talented, I'm so unsure of myself on the inside. They should only know. I feel like such a fake. I just do not want to continue living in this manner. There must be another way!"

Merle, too, has uneasy feelings about her self-worth. Why is her self esteem so often based on what and how much food enters her mouth, and/or what the scale reads. Why is it that our entire self-esteem, rather than being measured by who we are on the inside, is felt to only be measured by our appearance, and our ability to eat correctly? Intellectually, this may not make sense. However, emotionally and psychologically on some level, food and staying involved with our weight and dieting do have some advantages.

Food provides an elixir to uncomfortable feelings – feelings we may not know we have, or if we do, they may be so unpleasant that we will do anything to avoid them. Thoughts of food and weight serve as powerful distractors from thoughts and feelings about our lives. We have all learned, from a very young age, that food soothes our woes. I hate to admit this, but when my children were young, and in

I Always Start . . . .

a particularly crabby mood, I would offer them a cookie. It worked! They quieted down and seemed happier.

While we are eating we tend not to feel pain. If using food as a band-aid is occasionally done, it's not the end of the world. However, when practiced frequently, it does not allow us to deal with our inner feelings, our true selves.

As adults, issues such as marital discord, job dissatisfaction, a money crisis, parenting hardships, in-law troubles, dating difficulties, sickness, loneliness, and dozens of others are avoided when the majority of the day is centered around food/weight. In many ways, food, weight, and diets are easier and more socially comfortable to address than the aforementioned. Calling a friend to complain about your weight and your latest binge is much lighter than sharing feelings of hurt, loneliness, or anger.

Using food helps us combat stress and uncomfortable feelings and situations. You may be thinking, "but food and my weight cause me tremendous stress and discomfort!" My reply would be to agree, with a "but." Food/weight is a very tangible, concrete problem, with a tangible, concrete solution.

The solution seems to be, "I need to lose 25 pounds and then I'll be happy, feel good, meet my mate...," and on the surface this seems pretty simple. So the plan is formulated: "I will just eat less! As I eat less, my weight will come off, and I will feel happy."

That is supposed to be the plan. However, what if there were some other issues in your life? What if a bad job is causing you a great deal of stress? You have bills to pay, so you can't simply quit. What if you are in an unfulfilling marriage? You can't walk away from it, you have two children and a mortgage payment. Do you simply say, "Okay, I'm out of here?" The answer to either of these examples would have to be thought out, discussed with family and friends, and planned thoroughly.

Life's decisions are difficult. Since I do not know anyone who has a perfect life, we all are continually faced with difficult situations and challenges. Human beings are fortunate to be able to feel joy, laughter, passion, security and warmth. It's also our fate to experience anger, hurt, sadness, frustration, guilt, and a wide variety of other uncomfortable feelings.

Most people accept, at least on an intellectual level, that experiencing a variety of emotions is part of being human. However, experiencing uncomfortable feelings is often so unbearable that the individual represses sad emotions. A decision is made, usually at a young age, to protect oneself from pain. This decision is a survival decision often from being raised in families where feelings were not validated, honored, or respected – not necessarily because the parents meant to hurt their children, but because their ability to deal with their own pain is limited.

I don't believe that parents stand up with a list of feelings that they teach their children are wrong or bad to feel. Somehow, we learn that if we share a certain kind of feeling, we will either be ignored or yelled at in a very demeaning manner. For example, Melissa, a client of mine, at the age of ten decided she wanted her hair long and to wear it in a pony tail. Her mother always loved short hair. Melissa felt that she was old enough to have her hair the way she wanted. So she began letting it grow and within a few months, she was able to wear it up in a pony tail. Each day she wore it that way, her mother either commented or frowned. This type of treatment wasn't good for Melissa.

The day my client was actually the most hurt was the day she needed to go to the hairdresser for a trim at the neighborhood salon. Her hairdresser began cutting. Melissa soon noticed that what started out as a trim began to look more like a cut. Melissa told her to stop cutting so much. The beautician replied, "But your mom called and said to cut quite a bit off."

• • •

A decision is made, usually at a young age, to protect oneself from pain. This is a survival decision often from being raised in families where feelings were not validated, honored, or respected.

• • •

Unfortunately, this type of insensitivity and disregard for another's feelings, especially our children's, is all too common. If you were raised in a family where your feelings, if different from your parents', were ignored, unsupported, and put down, you probably figured out at a young age not to admit to any like feelings. The result of sharing such feelings might have led to getting hurt, or feeling like a bad person. In each of our families, we learned what feelings were okay to express, and which ones were not. In most families, the "right" feelings to share might include love, caring, giving, or being nice. The "wrong" feelings to express might include anger, jealousy, frustration and hurt. Our parents were incorrect.

• • •

Feelings are not right or wrong; they just are.

• • •

Right now, as an adult, each time you experience a feeling that you label as wrong, or bad, you're judging yourself in the same way. Shortly after all this judging, do not be surprised if you notice an overwhelming urge to overeat. Here is where the eating acts as a viable substitute for feelings. Dealing with food/weight, although not pleasant, does allow uncomfortable inner feelings to stay tucked away. The place where these feelings are kept gets filled up quickly. Eventually, these feelings resurface. Until these feelings are dealt with in a healthy, direct manner, the urge to eat will continue to return.

It's very difficult to deal with these feelings in a healthy, direct manner, if each time they start surfacing, we push them away and tell ourselves that we should not have them. We may label these feelings silly or bad. I often hear comments from clients similar to these.

"Jealous of my best friend's new house? Of course not! That's ridiculous, I'm so happy for her!"

"Why should I be angry at my sister? It's not a big deal that she didn't call me on my birthday. She is very busy."

"I am not hurt that my brother did not attend my son's high school graduation. He had an important dinner meeting."

"People are starving in Bosnia, how dare I feel such 'silly' feelings."

Feelings such as jealousy, anger and hurt may seem too petty to admit. This is the core of the problem. All feelings are important; none are silly or trivial. Each time these feelings or any others are discarded, denied, or labeled as wrong, silly or bad – your soul and identity are put down. Soon after, cookies will start calling. As these feelings of hurt, anger, jealousy, loneliness and frustration start tugging at you, thoughts of food enter your field of consciousness. You may try to busy yourself with other things, but the thoughts generally persist. After all, they are there for a reason. If ignored, don't be surprised if you throw on a coat and zoom off to your favorite grocery store.

This is how people become emotional eaters and compulsive dieters. In an attempt to fight off a full range of feelings, we eat. Food may be the only comfort people know. The problem is that food is only a short-term comfort, and a band-aid to our pain. If you place a band-aid on a cut without cleaning it, it may feel better temporarily. However, if unattended the wound may fester and cause a great deal of long-term pain. The same is true with our emotional pain. If eating is used to repress feelings, you may feel better instantly. However, if they're ignored, in the long run, the pain deepens.

This pain is why people stay intertwined with food, weight, and diets. It's not because they lack willpower or are weak persons. People can binge, vomit, fast, obsessively exercise or eat excessive portions, rather than deal with their feelings.

It's important that you hear this – take it in. I have met the most interesting, creative, bright and talented people over the years. However, they didn't see these great qualities in themselves. People who have used food to help them deal with their lives, have picked a coping mechanism that worked. It made them feel better, enabling them to cope with other parts of their life. The problem is that this coping mechanism also has some negative side effects including extra weight (with all of its inherent health problems), feeling out of control and badly about oneself.

• • •

It's not because they lack willpower or are weak persons. People can binge, vomit, fast, obsessively exercise or eat excessive portions, rather than deal with their feelings.

• • •

The extra weight alone constitutes a potentially severe health hazard, with heart attack and stroke two of the more obvious dangers. Add high blood pressure to the mix, and the physical risk of over weight combines with the negative emotional factors to make food an unhealthy coping mechanism.

Please be assured that your eating urges, your preoccupation with food, diets, and your weight do have a cause. Here is what the pattern looks like:

Each time you have an overwhelming urge to overeat..an urge that you are fairly certain is not about physical hunger, an urge that seems to come from nowhere – there has been a precipitating situation or thought that has left you feeling uncomfortable. This feeling is one that you presently believe is wrong to experience. It's a feeling you believe you "should" not feel and you judge it as wrong and yourself as bad. As you keep this feeling suppressed, you start feeling stressed. Soon after, you crave food. You eat, feel guilty, and promise this is the last time. But since situations, thoughts, and feelings continually occur, so does the cycle. (See chart on page 50)

What kind of feelings might cause a particular person to crave food? As previously mentioned, for each of us it may be different, depending on our families. A generic rule of thumb to follow is this: any feelings that were considered taboo in your household are probably feelings you have difficulty experiencing today.

This reminds me of Mary, a homemaker with three children all under the age of six. Before having children, she worked as a court reporter and loved it. Although she loved her children, she sometimes felt bored while staying home with them. She felt terrible for having these feelings of boredom, as a "good" mother would never experience this. On a really stressful day the ice cream would start to call while her youngest was napping.

What was Mary feeling? My guess was that she was feeling guilty about unfulfilled feelings. How could she feel this way? After all, she had a nice home, and a healthy family. This is a great example of denial. Whether she was "supposed" to feel some empty feelings or not, the reality was, she did. These feelings did not mean that she did not love her children or feel blessed by them. However, she had difficulty allowing herself to feel both sets of feelings.

Accepting that she has these particular feelings is the first step in addressing them. Many people have rules about motherhood, friendship, career and marriage. For each of these situations, we are supposed to feel certain sets of feelings. God forbid, a series of feelings surface that is not on our agenda! There have been many times in my office when a client of mine begins to get in touch with some feelings that she feels she is not supposed to have. Shortly, she may begin to look in her purse for some gum.

Unfortunately, these uncomfortable feelings are a part of life. This is a fact. When you go to the dentist, you may feel a bit anxious. I know I do! You have gone through it enough times, however, to know that the cleaning may be a bit uncomfortable, or the Novocaine may be annoying. But upon completion, you feel fine. You have learned from past experience. Your experience with feelings is not so well-honed, even the negative ones. We learn that painful things do happen, and time heals most wounds. This is something that you need to learn and believe.

As we reflect on our lives, all have experienced painful feelings, whether it's having been left out at a party, being rejected by a love interest, not getting into a desired school or club, or even the early death of a loved one. If we were allowed and able to process these feelings and be comforted by our loved ones, being with uncomfortable feelings as adults, though not pleasant, would be much more tolerable. Painful experiences do occur, but with love, nurturing and time, these feelings will dissipate as they heal. It is important to both understand and experience when we can deal with our emotions in a healthy and mature manner, inappropriate food consumption will also dissipate and heal. Almost every situation and relationship in our life bring up mixed feelings. Letting yourself feel feelings, and deal with them accordingly, is the true prescription to weight management and positive self-image.

• • •

Remove all labels of "wrong" or "bad."

• • •

I Always Start . . . .

In order to get in touch with the feeling you are suppressing, reflect on the behaviors that were considered taboo in your family. For example, you might have come from a family of yellers and screamers. Your parents might have loved a good fight. But if everyone in that family came home with a problem that involved hurt feelings, he/she might have received the message that exhibiting angry feelings was acceptable, but expressing hurt ones was clearly not okay. If you were feeling hurt or vulnerable, you probably would have been reprimanded, perhaps even called a name like "baby" or "sissy." You might have been reminded of all the people who have it worse, and how dare you whine. Off to your room you were sent. Clear messages were learned, "I hurt, but I shouldn't; therefore, I am bad."

Feelings, as I have said, are funny. We may try large doses of rationalizations and self-deceptions to keep those scary, unacceptable feelings from surfacing. We may be adept enough to keep them out of our consciousness, enabling them to be productive. These feelings need to be addressed. Diets are not broken because a person is weak or stupid. Good intentions fall by the wayside because they are directed toward the symptom, food, rather than the cause, feelings. This is why so-called diets do not work. No one can eliminate all uncomfortable situations, thoughts, and feelings. The trick is to intervene with healthy alternatives before you reach a stress level that causes you to turn to your standby, food. A healthier way to proceed when situations/thoughts bring on uncomfortable feelings might look more like this:

A situation or thought occurs and some uncomfortable feelings arise. You are able to get in touch with these feelings. Addressing them in a healthy, non-judgmental manner, you remove all labels of "wrong" or "bad."

You find a way that feels appropriate to deal with the feelings. You feel better. Hence, the urge to eat disappears. (See chart on page 51)

Feelings Are Not Right Or Wrong — They Just Are

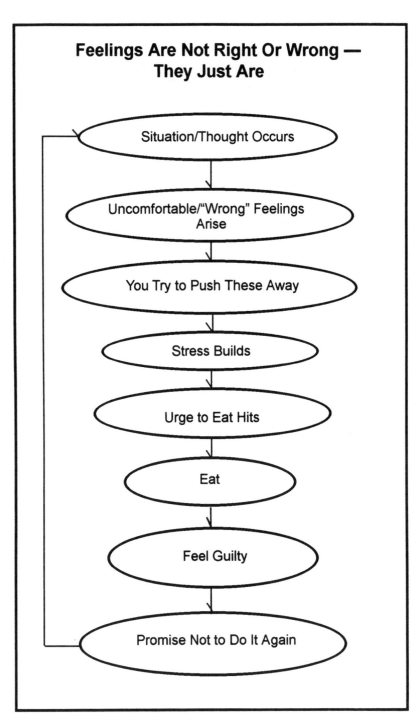

Situation/Thought Occurs

Uncomfortable/"Wrong" Feelings Arise

You Try to Push These Away

Stress Builds

Urge to Eat Hits

Eat

Feel Guilty

Promise Not to Do It Again

FEELINGS ARE NOT RIGHT OR WRONG —
THEY JUST ARE.

So here is how it looks!

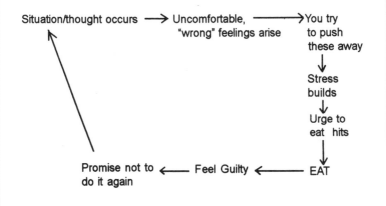

Situation/thought occurs ⟶ Uncomfortable, ⟶ You try
"wrong" feelings arise to push
these away

↓

Stress
builds

↓

Urge to
eat hits

↓

Promise not to ⟵ Feel Guilty ⟵ EAT
do it again

▬ ▬ ▬ ▬ ▬ ▬ ▬

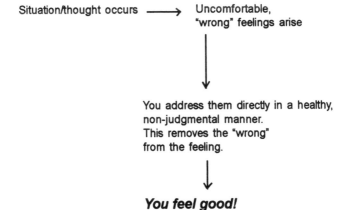

Situation/thought occurs ⟶ Uncomfortable,
"wrong" feelings arise

↓

You address them directly in a healthy,
non-judgmental manner.
This removes the "wrong"
from the feeling.

↓

You feel good!

When you can identify unsettling situations and the thoughts and feelings they trigger, and can accept that these feelings are neither "bad" nor "wrong," you can deal with them effectively without food. This time, your changes will be permanent. Living life without food and weight on your mind every minute is possible.

The chapters that follow cover the ways to succeed in this process. Every now and then, check with your gut instinct to see if what you're learning makes sense. As you begin to eliminate old rules about feelings and eating, the urges to overindulge will be sent on their way. The realization that you can replace emotional desires for food with the desire for self-care and self-love, is an important step in reaching your desired body weight – and inner peace.

Chapter Four

The Feeling Journal

Y*ou now need to focus* your attention on identifying what kind of situations, thoughts, and feelings trigger your eating response. For each of us, these are different. However, the messages experienced are the same for all: we think we are "wrong" or "bad" for certain feelings.

Most of the things that can trigger an eating urge are generally day-to-day life occurrences. The feelings or situations are not usually catastrophic! That is why it's often difficult to identify. Our feelings are subtle. I want to go back to the luncheon incident I described in the first chapter. My girlfriend did not have any diet cola at her luncheon. Alone, this "should" not have been that big a deal – please note that dangerous word in quotes! Right or wrong, I certainly was upset. It wasn't just about the diet cola. Rather, it was related to our friendship, closeness, jealousy, and sensitivity. These feelings I labeled as silly, and childish. I focused on the diet cola, and how I "should" be able to go an afternoon without diet pop and be fine. The more I suppressed my true feelings of hurt and anger concerning the friendship, the more I ate.

These are the kinds of situations I want you to be looking for in your everyday life. Often I have heard clients say, "Everything in my life is good. Why should I be using food in such an unhealthy way?" As we begin to explore their day-to-day lives, there are always some underlying issues that are bothering them. Nothing necessarily huge, but something they are concerned about that they probably feel "should" not be upsetting them. Since we don't want to deal with these issues, we do anything to avoid them, especially eat, or try some new diet fad. Staying food and diet absorbed ensures that life's discomforts – that I believe are meant to be there to wake us up and take notice – are ignored.

I Always Start . . . .

Another example that comes to mind is Sheila. Sheila is the mother of four daughters ranging in age from four to fourteen. She is happily married and is in a fortunate enough financial position where she does not have to work. She lives in a lovely home, and has a housekeeper once a week. What could possibly be wrong with Sheila's life? Her children, thank God, are healthy. She has a beautiful home, and a wonderful husband. As we began our sessions together, it became evident that there were times when her kids annoyed her. What a surprise! Occasionally, they all needed her attention at once. They would often fight with each other over the pettiest things. This really wore on her. She sometimes wished that she could just be alone. All of these frustrating feelings, and others, Sheila felt awful about owning.

As we explored further into her childhood, I learned that her mother was less than perfect. Her father died when she and her sister were teenagers. Sheila's mother fell apart. It became Sheila's job to take care of her mother, who began drinking and dating many men. As her own pain regarding her unhealthy parenting surfaced, it became clear how much pressure she placed on herself to be the "perfect" mother, always there for her children, and never impatient. Certainly, an impossible task for anyone!

On the surface, Sheila's life appeared fine, and in some ways it was true. However, as with any emotional eater, there is always something going on internally. It is this "stuff" that needs to be addressed. No one's life is perfect or clear cut. Not acknowledging these equivocations and mixed feelings leads to continuous involvement with food, weight, and diets, as well as not reaching our potential. The time and energy we focus on false issues keep us from living our lives more fully, and from devoting our resources to the real issues in our lives.

● ● ●

There is always something going on internally. It is this "stuff" that needs to be addressed.

● ● ●

Acknowledging our feelings must be precipitated by awareness. This is the first and most important step in change. I've heard people say, "I don't know what I'm feeling. I just know I want something sweet!" Here is a tool to help you identify with your feelings. Your goal is to do what I recommend. Remember, any kind of insight or new behavior can be both exciting and uncomfortable, so the first set of feelings to deal with is this discomfort. Know that it's normal and appropriate to be uneasy. Do not put yourself down; never tell yourself that you "should" not feel this way.

To help you in becoming aware of your feelings, particularly those that most often push you toward food, I want you to begin keeping a feeling journal. This is not a food journal. However, it's fine if you want to keep a separate journal of everything you eat.

I want you to buy an attractive, bound writing book. I want this journal to be your new best friend. Keeping this journal will help you get in touch with your inner self. Instead of spending hours thinking and worrying about food, you'll be thinking and worrying about you.

This is a very important shift – this focus on yourself rather than food and everyone else in your life. As you explore yourself, calculate how much time you're devoting to yourself. In my experience, most people with eating and weight issues are not very good at caring for themselves. They feel it is selfish. However, it's quite on the contrary. The more you attend to your own needs, the easier it is to cater to others. On airplanes, flight attendants give instructions about using emergency oxygen, clearly stating that those traveling with children should place masks on themselves first, allowing them to better assist their children. It is healthy to give to yourself. Furthermore, it helps boost self-esteem, and feels better than constantly giving to others. "If they like us, then we must be okay!" Being a giver is a common characteristic of an emotional eater. There's nothing wrong with giving; however, there should be balance. In most cases, there isn't. So we give disproportionately, then later find ourselves eating. Why? When we constantly give to others, we often feel angry and resentful, followed by feeling guilty for such feelings.

• • •

This is a very important shift – this focus on yourself rather than food and everyone else in your life.

• • •

I am not suggesting that in order to recover from your eating and weight issues, you need to become an egotistical creep. I am saying that excessive generosity is a major characteristic of people with weight problems. The word "no" is rarely in their vocabulary. For example, I had a client who stayed home with her two children, ages three and six. Jill's neighbor's husband was unemployed, and had two children, ages four and eight. Each day after school, Jill's neighbor would bring his children over and ask if she minded watching them while he ran some errands. She really did mind, but she pitied him because he was unemployed. Jill felt "bad" saying no, even though his children were not her favorite, and even though she wanted to devote her afternoons to herself and her own children. We often tend to accept being inconvenienced over inconveniencing someone else. Jill wound up saying "yes" to her neighbor, enabling her to stay needy and overly concerned about being liked, later using food to camouflage her feelings.

Another common characteristic to look for in yourself, as you begin this journal process, is perfection. Do you find that everything you do has to be just perfect? I had a client who was hosting Thanksgiving dinner for 30 people. Someone offered to bring cut-up vegetables and a dip for an hors d'oeuvre. She declined, fearing the vegetables would not be cut to her liking. This need to be perfect goes hand-in-hand with wanting to be accepted and liked by others. We first need to like and accept ourselves. We need not worry so much about what others think. We can't please everyone. Not everyone has to be fond of us. By the same token, we don't like everyone we meet. This does not mean the person is awful or terrible. He/she may have many people they're close to. The same is true for ourselves.

Paralleled with this perfectionism and the need to be accepted is the tendency to see things only as black or white; relationships are all or nothing, whether it be with food or with friends. I urge you to see the gray areas as well. You need to see things from several angles. Allow yourself to have mixed emotions about yourself, others, and life.

Others tend to see us as pillars of strength, laying their troubles at our doorstep. They compliment us on how well we handle everything. When others are in a bind, they have no qualms about calling us. We wind up endlessly listening to their "jams," hanging up and literally eating them up with some peanut butter.

Many people who use food to deal with their feelings have difficulty coping with conflict. Avoiding conflict complements our need to always be nice, hence, our need to be liked. However, conflict is a part of life. Instead of trying to rationalize these moments away and eating, we need to address them directly and see them as the learning and growth opportunities they are. Peace, at all costs, is not a motto I would support. The cost is yourself.

Being a mind reader is another characteristic for which to be watchful. We are so busy taking care of everyone else's wants, that we know in advance what they need. Nine out of ten times we are correct. We then get disappointed, or hurt that they can't read our wants and desires. Not telling them is the problem. The more we use our mouths to express feelings, or needs, the less our mouths will be used for eating.

While you are using your journal to reflect, you need to examine where you fit on the continuum of these characteristics. Are you the giver in your family all of the time? Do you try to perfect everything you do? Do you have the tendency to see in only black or white? Are you the caretaker in the immediate world, except for yourself? The answers to these questions are correlated to your eating behaviors.

Again, I am not suggesting that you need to change your entire personality to be at an appropriate weight, and eat normally. In the 1970s there was a lot written on assertiveness training. People were told that they must tell everyone in their life how they feel in order to feel good about themselves. People were telling their aunts, uncles, brothers, parents, and even the grocery clerks their innermost feelings. It wasn't long until they noticed that no one was talking to them. I don't recommend that you practice this to such extremes. The goal here is not to put our feelings and needs above everyone else. Rather, allow ours to be equal. Ironically, I have found that the nicer we are to ourselves, the more giving and caring we can be to others. You need to reexamine your present rules about life and yourself. Some will remain the same, and some will need changing. Using your journal will help you sort out which are which.

As stated, the purpose of this journal is to help you get in touch with your feelings, especially when the urge to overeat strikes. Again, this urge to eat is not an accident, or generally about the food item(s) desired. This impulse is triggered by suppressed feelings, and needs to be closely examined. I want you to look at this urge in a new way – to see it as a barometer, an instrument that tells you that something is going on inside. Something that feels pretty uncomfortable. It is this something that occurs before you start thinking about ice cream.

For now you need to assume you're not in touch with these feelings. Just know what I am saying is true: *there is always a precipitating situation, thought, or feeling before you overeat.*

This feeling journal will be of extreme importance in assisting you in identifying the kind of situations, thoughts, and feelings that trigger your unhealthy eating episodes. Once you have learned to regularly write in and read your journal carefully, you'll be able to diagnose your entries and your feelings. This process will become the permanent key to unlocking the "why" of your desires to overeat.

Before you begin this process of searching, identifying, and dealing with your feelings, I want to remind you that this search will take time, effort, and perseverance. Going on a diet will seem easy in comparison to your present journey. However, the long-term benefits you'll receive from this experience will far surpass any you may have previously experienced from dieting. Please be patient with yourself. Your patience and perseverance will pay off. This pay-off will include appropriate weight, and a life free from "food on the brain." Even more importantly, it will include inner peace. Through the journaling process, you'll begin to have a choice. Right now the urge to eat strikes; although you try to fight it, eventually you give in. You begin to learn that you have a choice: *I can eat, or I can deal with what is bothering me.*

Thoughts of, "Oh, I have to eat right now," are replaced

with, "Ah Hah! I have the urge to overeat. There must be something uncomfortable I am feeling. I am going to have to look deeper into myself to discover what it is. At least I know that I am not crazy with this food thing!." This is the point where you'll now have a choice. "Do I eat, or do I deal with my feelings?"

The answer will always be up to you. Eating will always be an option. I do not know which you will choose. I do know that once you recognize what you're feeling, you will learn what you can do with these feelings to make you feel better, other than eat. Your urges will subside, this time permanently. Again, the choice will always be yours.

• • •
I can eat, or I can deal with what is bothering me.
• • •

It's time to start your journal. Here is what I want you to do. Each time you have this overwhelming urge to overeat, you are to write down the time of day, where you are, who you are with, and anything you can think of that might have upset you, or left you feeling uneasy – issues that you might have pretended did not bother you or you felt "should" not have bothered you in the past. So no matter how trivial or minor, write it down. If it's bothering you, it's neither trivial nor minor. Try to always keep in mind that these issues are important signals for your inner growth.

Next, write down what you are feeling at the moment. If you are not sure, guess. See the following listing of feelings on pages 63-64 to help you. Keep this in mind: the feelings that you are probably experiencing are ones judged and labeled "wrong" or "silly" in the past. You have felt like a bad person for having these feelings. Also remember you're going to be looking for a pattern of certain kinds of feelings that are the most unsettling. This way in the future you can deal with them in more direct, healthy ways, without food or diets. Initially, every situation can potentially trigger an eating situation. The final question is to ask yourself how will eating really help? In short, you may feel better, but in the long run the issues remain.

I hope I'm making myself clear about what I want you to write. If you are eating your three delicious meals and two snacks as recommended in the previous chapter, you shouldn't be hungry, and should be satisfied with your food in your palette and in your stomach. If you are having lunch and eat a cookie for dessert, this is not an urge to overeat. However, if you had a nice lunch at noon, and decided at one o'clock that another lunch would be good, start writing. If you want a scoop of ice cream, that is fine. If you eat an entire quart, however, it's time to pick up your pen. You may be thinking, "Once I have one, I need to eat everything, and I am not feeling anything uncomfortable. Is it just me, or is it just that I have bad habits?" Certainly, if you have been overeating for years, some of your excessive eating may be from bad habits (see page 87) but for right now, I would not be choosing things or having these food items in the house that are particularly enticing. I'm not saying that you can't ever have these foods, but be cautious. You are eating three good meals and two enjoyable snacks, including foods you love. Suddenly you have an overwhelming urge to overeat some cookies, which, until this point, you have been able to eat in moderation – look for those uncomfortable feelings!

I Always Start . . . .

The pages in your feeling journal should look like this:

Time: . . . .

Place: . . . .

Who I'm With . . . .

What happened, or what did I think about in the last one to five hours that has left me feeling uncomfortable, unsettled, or unanything: . . . .
. . . .
. . . .
. . . .

What am I feeling right now? . . . .
. . . .

How will eating really help? . . . .
. . . .

How often you need to write in your journal depends on how often you have the urge to overeat. If you are not having any major urges, then I recommend at least twice daily. You can write anything you wish about anything in your life.

Following is a list of feelings that can help you start.

I FEEL PLEASED

I FEEL IMPLICATED

I FEEL DEJECTED

I FEEL RELIEVED

I FEEL ADRIFT

I FEEL DULL

I FEEL AMUSED

I FEEL JITTERY

I FEEL SIMPLE

I FEEL BEAUTIFUL

I FEEL STRANGE

I FEEL RIDICULOUS

I FEEL HOPEFUL

I FEEL EXOTIC

I FEEL AFRAID

I FEEL DESIROUS

I FEEL SEGREGATED

I FEEL CAUTIOUS

I FEEL NOBLE

I FEEL DEAD

I FEEL SATISFIED

I FEEL INCONSISTENT

I FEEL VAIN

I FEEL COMMON

I FEEL INSOLENT

I FEEL UNEQUAL

I FEEL UNMATCHED

I FEEL SOCIABLE

I FEEL DISTINCTIVE

I FEEL HATEFUL

I FEEL MONOTONOUS

I FEEL LOVING

I FEEL STEREOTYPED

I FEEL FORGIVING

I FEEL METHODICAL

I FEEL PITIED

I FEEL GRIEF

I FEEL UNIQUE

I FEEL JEALOUS

I FEEL AGGRAVATED

I FEEL CONTENT

I FEEL KINDRED

I FEEL WEARY

I FEEL CHEERFUL

I FEEL ISOLATED

I FEEL UGLY

I FEEL WITTY

I FEEL ALIENATED

I FEEL VULGAR

I FEEL FASHIONABLE

I FEEL OUTLANDISH

I FEEL HOPELESS

I FEEL COURAGEOUS

I FEEL DETACHED

I FEEL COWARDLY

I FEEL WONDERFUL

I FEEL INTIMATE

I FEEL INDIFFERENT

I FEEL ANTAGONISTIC

I FEEL PROUD

I FEEL EXPECTANT

I FEEL BOASTFUL

I FEEL HOSTILE

I FEEL HUMBLE

I FEEL FRIENDLY

I FEEL MODEST

I FEEL DISCOURTEOUS

I FEEL COURTEOUS

I FEEL DREARY

I FEEL RESENTFUL

I FEEL PITIFUL

I FEEL SULLEN

I FEEL THREATENED

I FEEL RIGHTEOUS

I FEEL FAITHFUL

I FEEL REVENGED

I FEEL DUTIFUL

I FEEL ORIGINAL

I Always Start . . . .

I FEEL RESPECTABLE
I FEEL MOCKED
I FEEL HARMONIOUS
I FEEL CONTEMPT
I FEEL COMPATIBLE
I FEEL ACCUSED
I FEEL PURE
I FEEL REPUGNANT
I FEEL GUILTY
I FEEL ANGELIC
I FEEL HUMILIATED
I FEEL SENSUAL
I FEEL WORTHY
I FEEL CHILDISH
I FEEL IMPURE
I FEEL LOST
I FEEL JUDGED
I FEEL NONESSENTIAL
I FEEL NATURAL
I FEEL RESPONSIBLE
I FEEL MAD
I FEEL ANGRY
I FEEL WARY
I FEEL UPTIGHT
I FEEL PUT DOWN
I FEEL NERVOUS
I FEEL SHAKY
I FEEL DISCONTENTED

I FEEL ENVY
I FEEL FLATTERED
I FEEL WRONGED
I FEEL DISINTERESTED
I FEEL INNOCENT
I FEEL HAPPY
I FEEL SELFISH
I FEEL REWARDED
I FEEL IMPALED
I FEEL BADLY
I FEEL PIOUS
I FEEL CORNERED
I FEEL DRUNK
I FEEL EXHAUSTED
I FEEL PARENTED
I FEEL CONDEMNED
I FEEL PENALIZED
I FEEL SICK
I FEEL IRRELIGIOUS
I FEEL INCURABLE
I FEEL LOVABLE
I FEEL SAD
I FEEL LONELY
I FEEL STUPID
I FEEL SMALL
I FEEL PAINED
I FEEL IMPATIENT

You may want to add more.

Journaling will help you become more attuned to your emotions. Some people may be thinking, "I have the urge all day! Does that mean that I have to write every minute?" As you will probably find, some urges to overeat are more powerful and intense at different times than others. If you can, wait until the desire is at its strongest – then write.

It's extremely important to try and write before the food enters your mouth. This is when your feelings are the most intense. Sometimes, the desire is so strong that we eat first and then think about writing. If this occurs, go ahead and write after you have eaten.

The goal is to write. As mentioned earlier, before you eat, your feelings are right at the forefront. After you eat, these same feelings are more anesthetized. Therefore, they become more difficult to identify. If possible, try to write before you eat. This will allow you to get the maximum benefit from this process. But, even if you eat first, by all means, write!

• • •
Journaling will help you become more attuned to your emotions.
• • •

Also, do not worry about spelling, or punctuation, if your writing looks and sounds "right." Write whatever you are feeling. Few of us can come up with an exhaustive and enthralling analysis of our feelings the first time we try. That is perfectly fine.

Let's examine this scenario, and examples of Marcia's diary entries:

I Always Start . . . .

Marcia is a chronic dieter. She put on some extra weight and was feeling miserable. On a Monday, she decided to begin a new "diet." Her first thought each morning was, "I want to be good today. I am going to work hard to stay on my diet."

Fade to Marcia's kitchen. She has just finished her breakfast of plain cereal, skim milk, a small glass of juice, and coffee. Her two sons, ages 12 and 14, left the house in a rush, as they were late for school. They both left their half-eaten waffles on their plates. Marcia finds herself looking at the waffles, while the waffles were staring right back at her. The waffles were chanting, "Come eat me. You had a small breakfast. People are starving in Africa, don't waste." She picked up a corner of the waffle and brought it toward her mouth. She rationalized, "A little bite won't hurt." She took a bite, but panic struck. She quickly ran to the garbage disposal, spit the waffle out, and discarded the rest of the waffle. Marcia felt "good." She made it without cheating.

Later that day at work, Marcia had a confrontation with her boss. She has been employed by this company as a controller for five years. She enjoys her job, and always has excellent evaluations. Her boss often lacks tact. She has just finished her lunch containing three ounces of dry tuna, raw vegetables, a piece of fruit, two crackers, and a diet cola. She finds that her mind is drifting to the candy machine. She decides to walk over and peek at its contents. She begins the internal and eternal debate, "Should I, or shouldn't I, that's the question!" She pushes herself away, reminded that she is "dieting." Again, she feels "good" that she did not give in to her desires.

That evening at dinner, Marcia and her husband are trying to eat as their two sons are arguing about not liking the food. No one is too interested in how hard Marcia worked to fix a good, healthy dinner after working all day. She finds that her eyes are moving to the platter of chicken. The inner struggle begins again. She thinks, "One more piece of chicken is not the end of the world. At least it's not candy." Then, the other part of her kicks in, "I can't. If I want to lose weight, I have to be good." At last, the urge is too strong, and she grabs for a piece of chicken, promising herself, that this will be all. From that point, she continues to eat cookies, ice cream, and whatever else she finds.

Later that evening, Marcia is lying in bed filled with self loathing. She feels fat, and depressed. Her entire review of the day revolves around what, and how she ate. She feels horrible, promising herself that tomorrow will be a "good" day.

During Marcia's entire day, not once did she ask herself how she was feeling. She stayed food and diet oriented, choosing a bland and boring menu. No attention was paid to how she was feeling about her children, work, and family responsibilities or her unsatisfying meals. Had she kept a feeling journal, she may have written the following:

Time: 8:30 a.m.
Place: Home
Who am I with? Alone
What happened, or did I think about in the last one to six hours that left me feeling uncomfortable, unsettled, or unanything? The only thing that I can think of is how I hate when the kids are late and they leave their half-filled plates on the table rather than dumping them and placing them in the sink. I feel like I'm their maid! They're old enough to be responsible for their own dishes. On the other hand, they're

just kids. Maybe I expect too much.

What am I feeling right now? I'm not sure. Maybe a little angry at the kids, and a little guilty that I'm angry. I do know that I want those waffles, soggy and all!

How will eating these waffles really help me deal with myself or others? It won't, and I know that intellectually, but I still want the waffles! I hated my breakfast!

Time: 2:00 p.m.

Place: Work

Who am I with? Co-workers

What happened... My boss has really been irritating me. He talks to me like I'm 10 years old! I know I need to discuss how I feel with him, but I don't want to.

What am I feeling right now? I want candy! I also feel badly about the way I was spoken to and that I have not stood up for myself.

How will eating candy really help me deal with myself and my boss? It will get my mind off work! Other than that, I know it won't do anything, and I will feel terrible.

Time: 7:30 p.m.

Place: Home

Who am I with? My family

What happened... The boys are fighting, which really irritates me. I also feel no one appreciates me!

What am I feeling right now? Like I'm being childish for feeling unappreciated. I also feel as though I'm a wimp for not standing up for myself and making the kids be quiet. And the chicken is looking good!

How will eating chicken really help me deal with myself and others? It won't, in the long run. It will, however, for a little while, feel good.

As you can see, there is more to Marcia's desires than food, though, since her meals were rather bland, there probably were some actual issues of food deprivation. The same is probably true with your desires. As Marcia and you plan more satisfying meals, get more in touch with troublesome situations, and the connected feelings, and deal with these in new, direct and healthy ways, the desires for the food items are reduced, as will your body weight.

As you begin your own journal, I want to remind you again that the kind of things that can stir up an eating urge are, as with Marcia's life, day-to-day issues. If you suppress feelings such as anger at your children, boss or mate and feel you "shouldn't" have these feelings, urges to overeat will appear. Whether the issues concern children, work, parents, or friends, try to be as honest with yourself as possible. Your feelings are your feelings. By honoring and validating them, you are honoring and validating yourself.

Another client comes to mind. Sarah is a free-lance writer. She was just offered a job to edit a book. Initially, she was very excited. However, a half-hour after the offer, she noticed that she was in the kitchen eating. When she came in for our session, we began processing ALL of her feelings about this new endeavor. Sarah began sharing feelings of uncertainty. Could she really do a good job? She has so much other stuff going on right now, would she have enough time to really do an adequate job? As she shared her concerns, there was always a very quick, "yes but..." This was followed by, "Yes, but this is a great opportunity...Yes, but I'm being silly for worrying...Yes, but I shouldn't feel anxious. I really am being silly. Yes, but..."

Any time you have a situation in your life and you tell yourself that you are being silly, or that you shouldn't be feeling a certain way, you have just increased the chances of an eating episode. Again, your feelings are your feelings and are there to guide you. It is being able to decipher and process them in healthy ways that is essential.

Each entry shouldn't take more than about five minutes. If you would like to write longer, that's fine. Do not feel pressured. Sometimes, people say that they don't know when they're feeling uncomfortable, so how will they know when to write.

● ● ●

Your feelings are your feelings and are there to guide you.

● ● ●

I have two guidelines. One, as I have already suggested, to write when the urge to overeat hits. This is the feeling of having to eat whatever the item is, knowing that you're not really hungry, and feeling that you have to have it all. The other time to write is when you are experiencing what I call a distress sign. These are physical cues or anxious indicators in your body.

When upset or uncomfortable, most of us feel something in our body. I get a nervous stomach. Some people get sweaty palms, heart palpitations, a stiff neck, or they withdraw or start chatting. Right now, when you are under some kind of discomfort, you experience something in your body. This reaction often occurs before the urge to eat happens. If you can get in touch with this physical cue and write, it will ward off an eating binge.

For example, if you notice you occasionally get sweaty palms, it may not be long before you put two and two together. *Sweaty palms = uncomfortable situation = uncomfortable feelings which I better add up before the sum is eating!*

Keeping this collection of incidents and feelings plus having an awareness of your physical distress signals, are the beginning essential steps in learning to answer the important questions of WHY you overeat, and what you can do about it.

The journal alone will not take away your life issues by itself. Even if it could, in five years, new issues will present themselves. The journal and diagnosing your entries will assist you in becoming aware of what your feelings are, and how you presently deal with them. You will then be ready to move on to the next steps of changing these old patterns, replacing them with new, long-term, healthy ones.

Keep your diary for one week. After your week of entries, go back and reread what you wrote. Jot down what you notice about your feelings, life situations, and distress signals. Next, you'll develop skills which will help you diagnose your own feelings.

Chapter Five
Diagnosing Your Feelings

Now *that you've kept your diary for a week,* you're ready to look at what your entries mean. You have probably already begun to notice new feelings. Some of these feelings have felt more intense than others. I hope that you have begun to see a correlation between these more intense feelings and the overwhelming urge for food. Each time this urge manifests, flashers, sparklers, and blinkers need to be going off in your head, screaming, "Stop! This is an uncomfortable feeling happening: don't eat it...Examine it!"

Analyzing your feelings is not always an easy process. You might notice that you feel a little unsure or a bit scared about what you are writing. Anytime we approach something new and unknown, we all feel frightened. Feeling scared is normal. Do you remember when you started your first job? Exploring yourself is no less challenging. Learning to be attuned to your inner gut feelings can be initially unnerving. In the long run, it will not only feel good, but it will feel right.

When we respect and honor our inside soul, this gut feeling, our lives always feel better. Writing is important, so stay with the process. It is this process that allows you to see and be with your feelings. They are there in black and white. No more denial. Although this may be uncomfortable, it is the core of ending the vicious battle with food, diets, and weight.

As we begin to analyze your journal entries by paying close attention to different kinds of situations and thoughts, you'll be able to see that most of your feelings can be labeled in two primary categories. It will be the category that you have the MOST difficulty labeling as appropriate which presently causes you the most discomfort and probably the most urges to overeat. This dividing of feelings into two categories should assist you in diagnosing them more rapidly.

● ● ●

This is an uncomfortable feeling happening: don't eat it...Examine it!

● ● ●

One set of feelings will be labeled OUTWARD-VIGOROUS. These are feelings that are generally directed toward others (outward). In addition, they're usually quite harsh (vigorous). Feelings that fit into this category would include anger, jealousy, irritation, frustration, and intolerance. If you were to picture a lion and some of the feelings he exhibits, you would be in touch with these kinds of feelings.

The other set of feelings will be labeled INWARD-VULNERABLE. These feelings are usually softer (vulnerable) in nature, and are directed towards oneself (inward). Some examples of these former feelings are hurt, sadness, loneliness, inadequacy, helplessness, fear, and disappointment. If you were to picture a soft, comforting teddy bear it would assist you in picturing these types of feelings.

For every situation or thought that presents itself in our lives, we experience *both* sets of feelings. What is important to see is that one set is generally more painful and unacceptable than the other set. The more painful and less acceptable feelings are those which we label as "wrong." Although the other set may also be difficult to acknowledge, accept, or express, it is not as extreme as the "wrong" set. Your mission is to discover which set gives you the most difficulty.

Where did we get the message that some feelings are right to feel and some are wrong? For most of us, these lessons were learned in our families. This is not to say, as earlier mentioned, that each of our parents got up in front of us with a blackboard drawing up a list of "okay" feelings, and "not okay" feelings to have. But through words, looks, body language and actions, the messages were sent and received. For example, if you came from a family of yellers and screamers, these angry, loud feelings probably felt pretty familiar to you. For this reason, you may have very little difficulty dealing with outward-vigorous feelings. In your family, there was not a negative judgement placed upon expressing loud, and angry feelings. In this same family, softer, more fragile feelings, like hurt or sorrow, resulting in crying, were probably not seen favorably. As previously mentioned, one might have been labeled a "baby," or "weak" if these softer feelings were expressed. You learned to hide inward-vulnerable feelings. If this is how your family was, it would be highly likely that you're pretty adept in dealing and expressing your anger. On the other hand, you probably kept your softer, more fragile feelings suppressed. These vulnerable feelings most often send you to the pantry.

You need to look inside yourself and your family to see what kind of rules were taught. If "good" people never get angry and yell, then you may have difficulty with your anger. You may tend to judge yourself as "bad." If you think that anyone who cries is a "baby," chances are, the next time you have a tear in your eye, a negative judgment will be made. Keep in mind that you may intellectually understand that this is ridiculous.

Of course, all feelings, including anger and hurt, are normal. However, when you're turning to food, this is not an intellectual response, but an emotional one. Remember, it's the set of feelings that you have the most difficulty acknowledging that is causing the food to be so alluring. The times that you are feeling these "taboo" feelings are when food feels so comfortable...at least temporarily.

To assist you in examining your family rules, consider the following scenario:

75

I Always Start . . . .

You are ten years old and in the fifth grade. On Tuesday, you went to school, and your teacher was really on your back. She yelled at you unjustly. You were ordered to clean the entire classroom. Leaving to go to the washroom was forbidden. You left school feeling furious. The following day, your friends were agitating you, making fun of your shoes, and making rude comments. They even chose you last for the kickball team. You later found out that you weren't invited to one of the kid's birthday parties. You left school on the verge of tears.

The question I want you to ask yourself is which one of these experiences would you be most likely to share with your mother or father when you returned home? Think about your answer and try to go with your gut instinct.

If your answer is that you would have easily discussed the situation when you were angry, but would be hesitant to talk about the one by which you were hurt, you may still be living by those same rules. Anger towards others (outward-vigorous) is okay, and would be easier for you. However, feelings of hurt and sadness (inward-vulnerable) were more difficult to express.

Again, even if you understand intellectually that all feelings are fine, if you have a deep emotional "should not feel" message, eating urges will abound with said feelings. Each time you judge or deny a feeling, WATCH OUT, REFRIGERATOR!

You may be thinking you would not have shared either set of feelings with your parents. There are many people who come from families where almost all feelings were negated. This does not mean that you judge every feeling as "wrong," and therefore, eat for every emotion that you have ever experienced. It does mean, however, that you need to dig deeper to find which feelings are the most uncomfortable.

Whatever these feelings are and how you interpret them are the ones that are most apt to cause you to overeat.

Here is an example of how suppressed feelings lead to eating urges:

A mother of two small children, ages two and five, came to see me. She had a chronic weight problem her entire life. She was constantly battling the same 35 pounds, trying diet after diet. Her thoughts were consumed by food and her weight. She was tired of living this way and wanted to change.

After several sessions, it became clear through her journal entries and our sessions, that she had several "rules" regarding what a good mother was. Her entries were filled with situations where she felt she did not behave properly with her children...or should I say "perfectly?"

At one particular session, she told me that her daughter had the flu. The previous night, the younger child had thrown up four times. This meant that mother had to change the linens repeatedly. Each time the younger child awoke, the older one asked for, the all too common, one last glass of water. She finally lost her patience, snapping at both kids, telling them to get into bed. Alas, just as she had finally thought everyone was taken care of and in bed, her youngest child had one more episode. She got up, attended to her child and then headed for the kitchen and finished last night's leftovers.

Let's examine what caused this urge for the leftovers. One guess might be the overwhelming frustration that the mother felt. As she openly discussed these feelings, I probed deeper. Remember, always look for the less obvious feelings. I was looking for which feelings she was experiencing and then quickly judging as wrong, and not okay. The judged feelings are always the precipitators to an eating urge. It wasn't that she felt awful that she was angry and frustrated. There was a part of her that knew that anyone who had been up four or five times in the middle of the night would have these feelings. What seemed NOT OKAY was that she vented them. A "good" mother would have remained calm, caring and soothing throughout the night.

This woman was falling short of some ideal that she had set up for herself in her role as a mother. Rather than acknowledging and accepting her anger and letting some of it out, (as long as it was not abusive), she labeled herself as a "bad" mother. She felt horrible about herself, and turned to food.

It was clear that she had an easier time getting in touch with outward-vigorous feelings. It was much harder for her to deal with more vulnerable-inward feelings about herself.

In our sessions, we worked on shifting some of her unrealistic expectations and challenged her judgements and values about what a "good" mother and person looks like. The more attuned she became to her softer feelings, and learned to address them in a kind, nurturing manner, the less she needed to use food for comfort. Instead of thinking about food and weight all day, she began thinking about herself, her role as a mother, and what she wanted in the future. Dealing with life, rather than food, although sometimes unsettling, is what we all need to do in the long run.

Another example might look like this:

> It's 10 p.m., often a difficult time for emotional overeaters. Sam has been dieting and has lost 20 pounds. He needs to lose at least another twenty, for health and physical reasons. Evenings have always been the most difficult time for him. His wife, Sarah, knows how well he has been doing, and that the evenings have always been his favorite snack time.
>
> On this particular evening, Sarah is on the phone. Sam watches TV. Sarah has been on the phone for two hours. Sam asked her twice to get off the phone and join him in watching one of their favorite programs.

He wanted to spend time with her. As a fairly liberated man and a considerate husband, he understood that after work and preparing dinner, she may need time for herself.

His thoughts went something like this: "I should understand, and not feel left out, unimportant, or uncared about." However, it's not long before he finds himself eating a large bowl of buttered popcorn. Rather than acknowledging and accepting his softer, inward-vulnerable feelings, and dealing with them and Sarah, he suppressed them and ate.

It was certainly not Sarah's fault that Sam turned to food. Sam denied his feelings and "pretended" that they were not important. He talked himself out of his feelings. This subterfuge of feelings always is the key ingredient to any food intake. It's extremely important to be in touch with your own self-talk as you become more aware of your feelings and how you process them.

For practice in reviewing your entries and assisting you in becoming aware of your own feelings and self-talk, try to diagnose an actual entry from one of my clients. We will call her Jane. Jane has recently gained some weight. She has always had 10 pounds extra, but now, it was up to 25 pounds. She was extremely distressed. As you read her entries, see if you can figure out which category of feelings she has the most difficulty dealing with. Read each section carefully. Try to read between the lines, and discover her "true" feelings.

Time: 10:00 a.m.
Place: Home
Who am I with? Alone
What happened or what did I think about in the last one to five hours that left me feeling uncomfortable, uneasy or unanything? The kids are driving me crazy. I made their beds

and they unmade them. They were late for the bus, and I had to drive them to school. On the way home I wanted to stop at the bank, and there was tons of construction. I had to forget about going to the bank. When I walked in the door, the phone was ringing, and it was my friend, Judy, cancelling our lunch date for the tenth time. She had a business appointment, as usual.

What am I feeling right now? Like I want to eat. It's only 10:00 in the morning. My entire day is empty. I want to eat lunch now! I hate having to worry about what and when I'm going to eat or not. I hate myself!

How will eating really help me deal with myself, or others? I really don't know or care right now, I just want to eat!

Time: 2:30 p.m.
Place: Home
Who am I with? Alone
What happened... Nothing I can think of. I have been eating all day long. Back and forth, snooping in the refrigerator. I'm not even hungry, or eating things I like. I'm just eating to eat. The children will be home soon. John called and said that he would be late. He's playing tennis, which I understand he enjoys. I hate when he comes home really late. I do not know what I'm supposed to do with myself for the rest of the day and evening. Then, I begin thinking about all of the good things in my life, why can't I just be happy?

What am I feeling right now? Nervous and stuffed!

How will eating help me deal with myself or others? I know it doesn't, so why do I keep doing it?

* * *

Take a moment to really examine Jane's entries. See if you can diagnose which feelings she is desperately trying to cover and deny. Divide all the feelings you see into outward-vigorous, and inward-vulnerable. Try to read past her words, into her inner gut. The more you can see Jane's feelings, the more you'll be able to see your own.

Let's look at Jane's first entry and divide it into the two categories. If we begin with the outward-vigorous feelings it seems evident that she's feeling pretty hostile toward her children. These feelings she is able to own up to without any negative judgements.

Her ability to see that all parents get angry and frustrated with children is present. How does she really feel about her friend Judy's business appointment? Keep in mind that Judy is a dear friend, and Jane does care a lot about her. Inside, Jane may have been confronted with jealous and angry feelings toward a good friend. Is it okay to have these kinds of feelings? The answer is, right or wrong, we all do.

In addition, Jane probably felt guilty about feeling these angry, jealous feelings – after all, a good friend would never feel that way! Jane was also dealing with her own feelings about having a rather boring day. It was easier for Jane to zero in on hating her problem, than to deal with her resentment toward a good friend, and her own empty life.

These empty feelings that Jane was experiencing were her inward-vulnerable feelings. Looking at yourself and evaluating your life is never easy. Seeing Judy happy, busy, and feeling fulfilled brought to the forefront her purposeless feelings. Yes, she loved her kids and husband, but Jane seemed to yearn for more. Again, which is easier to deal with? Facing our own fears and making some life changes, or food? Eating, in the short-term, is always easier and less scary.

The second entry suggests a similar pattern. Jane is able to acknowledge her displeasure at John's tennis date and his lack of sensitivity to her day, and the responsibilities to the children. She also can acknowledge her mixed feelings about the children's return home from school. Her frustration and annoyance (outward-vigorous) are acknowledged and accepted.

However, her inward-vulnerable feelings of emptiness, uncertainty of how to emotionally take care of herself for the evening, and sadness that John wasn't there to comfort her, all stayed suppressed. She "should" be okay, and she knows that John does deserve an evening of tennis, so how dare she feel lonely or sad! Which would you rather deal with, an issue with your spouse, your inner self, or the refrigerator?

Jane had some clear messages that she was receiving. Being angry, annoyed, and frustrated, although not wonderful, were all tolerable. However feeling hurt, sad, lonely, and unsure were silly, wrong, and not okay. So it would follow, if she ever felt these feelings, she would feel awful about herself, and want to run from what she was feeling. Her way was to run to food.

As you begin diagnosing your own diary entries, it's important to look for what types of messages you are receiving and believing. These messages need to be decoded. A helpful way to become more attuned to your feeling messages is to listen to your self-talk. Our minds are always working. Our thoughts come and go throughout the day. What we are thinking and saying to ourselves is extremely powerful and influential. If all day you're thinking terrible things about yourself – "I'm fat. I'm ugly. I'm stupid" – you'll not feel too good about yourself. On the other hand, if you are able to talk to yourself in a loving, warm, caring, kind, and nurturing manner, generally how we treat others, by the day's end, you'll be feeling pretty good.

Getting in touch with your self-talk, and the messages this talk relays, and challenging these messages, will hasten the process of feeling-recognition and analysis. This self-talk often feels like a tape that never gets turned off. Thoughts and feelings are difficult to turn off, but they can be turned over and replaced with new and healthier ones. This is what keeping a feeling journal and analyzing and diagnosing your entries will begin to offer.

As you examine your entries, search to uncover feelings

that are difficult to admit having. As you are reading what you wrote, what are you thinking? Are you making judgements? Are you labeling your entries with negative adjectives? Are you able to notice what you're doing and how you are processing your examination of your own writings? Search for and explore difficult feelings. Try to discover how and where you keep your most uncomfortable feelings. The solution to overeating is the disclosure of your deepest emotions.

I want you to begin this week with writing as often as possible. Be aware that most eating urges, as with Jane, are most usually connected to feelings about yourself and significant others.

It's important to examine how often key people in your life are present, either physically, or in your thoughts, when you find yourself needing an extra large hot fudge sundae! This is why the question in your journal "Who am I with?" is included. For example, if you notice every time your boss steps into the room, you find your mind drifting to thoughts of luscious sweets, I would determine that you have some feelings about your boss that you want to avoid confronting. Or, if each time you visit your mom, you find yourself nibbling on anything, and everything, knowing that your mom is hardly Julia Child, and has even been known to cook things for so long that you aren't even sure what they are – I would again deduce that there are some unresolved issues between you and your mom!

• • •

It's important to examine how often key people in your life are present, either physically, or in your thoughts, when you find yourself needing an extra large hot fudge sundae!

• • •

Sometimes this self-exploration process is easier if you put your diary aside for awhile. Then pick it up and pretend that is a friend's. After all, we treat others well, so if we pretend it's not ours, we may be able to see more clearly and gently what we are feeling. Push yourself to look inside and see what kinds of feelings you are accustomed to avoiding and suppressing. Be patient with yourself. As with any new process, it takes time.

Please note that I now want you to include the two categories I have discussed. Your new entries will look like this:

Time: . . . .
Place: . . . .
Who am I with? . . . .
What happened or what did I think about . . . .
What am I feeling right now?
　　Outward-Vigorous: . . . .
　　Inward-Vulnerable: . . . .
How will eating help me deal with myself or others? . . . .
. . . .

The more able you are to get in touch with all your feelings, the better you'll feel about yourself. Hence, the less necessary food will feel. Below are two entries that I would like you to evaluate. See if you can determine what each person is really feeling, not just what they are disclosing. Fill in the blanks.

Entry #1
Time: 3:00 p.m.
Place: Home
Who am I with? Family
What happened or did I think about... There was just a huge rainstorm. I went down to the basement and there was over a foot of water! All of my computer equipment is down there. When I ran up to tell my husband, he didn't seem too concerned. His reaction was, "Not much we can do. We'll just have to do without. I guess you'd better bring your computer upstairs." I suppose he's right, even though his attitude bugs me. There really isn't that much down there and I have already heard on the radio that some people have lost much more. I guess I should be grateful, but all I want is potato chips!
What am I feeling right now?
　　Outward-Vigorous:
　　Inward-Vulnerable:
How will eating really help me deal with myself or others? Not much!

I Always Start . . . .

Entry #2
Time: 2:00 p.m.
Place: Office
Who am I with? Co-workers
What happened or did I think about? Everything seems to be going fine. I just completed a major project and my boss approved of it. He is not much for showering a person with praise. I know that this is just his disposition. I do feel bad – a little – but I know that I shouldn't feel this way. I'm so sensitive. All I know is that I want to finish all the sweet rolls in the coffee room.

What am I feeling right now?
Outward-Vigorous:
Inward-vulnerable:

How will eating help me deal with myself or others? I know that it won't, but I want to eat!

After reading these entries, my analysis looked like this:

ENTRY #1: Outward-vigorous: anger, and lots of it, at her husband and the flood. Inward-vulnerable: hurt, sad and a bit self-pitying.

Which seemed more difficult for her to honor? I think it was her sense of loss. She did not feel she had the right to feel bad because other people had it worse. Whether other people are in pain or not, ours is still ours. Minimizing feelings is never productive in the goal of emotional health.

ENTRY #2: Outward-vigorous: annoyed at her boss' lack of praise. Inward-vulnerable: hurt due to lack of appreciation.

Again, she did not validate her sensitivity and her need for appreciation. Somehow, she felt these feelings were silly. There is no such thing as a silly feeling. All feelings are important. As I continue to remind you, feelings are the pathways to who you are. To ignore and suppress them causes anger, discomfort and the urge to abuse food and self.

Through continued journaling, your ability to connect with your true inner self will grow.

A word about nighttime eating and "bad habits." Over the years, I've found one of the most common times of the day for excessive eating is the late evening. It's important to recognize that some of these nighttime food attacks, which may include emotional undertow, are bad habits. For example, if you have always watched the 10 p.m. news while eating a large bag of popcorn, like Pavlov's dogs, the news has become an automatic stimuli for eating. As already mentioned, a late night reasonable snack is fine, but if you are really over-snacking, this is where habit leaves and suppressed feelings arrive.

At night, we are more vulnerable. We're tired at the end of the day and want to relax. It's precisely due to this relaxed state that we are more vulnerable...to our feelings...Feelings that during the day we may have ignored. If you enjoy your snack late at night, that's fine, but be attuned to old habits and new feelings.

Chapter Six

Replacing Food with Healthier Alternatives

If you have been diligently journaling, you should be experiencing a higher level of feeling awareness. As I have previously stated, it's never an accident or coincidence when an overwhelming urge to overeat strikes. There is always some precipitating uncomfortable situation, thought, or feeling.

Have you been playing detective in trying to uncover your hidden clues to your emotions? Have you been examining each entry, looking for inward-vulnerable and outward-vigorous feelings? Are you aware of which set of feelings is most difficult for you to acknowledge?

If your answer to these questions is in the affirmative, then you should be feeling pretty proud of yourself! Perhaps you may still be a bit nervous or unsure. It's perfectly normal. This nervousness can also be a sense of pride. Remember that looking at yourself is never a particularly easy and comfortable process. It is, however, one of the most fulfilling – without gaining a pound!

Through your writings, you have already gathered a substantial amount of key information. This information will present patterns of thoughts, feelings, and behaviors that contribute to your eating urges.

Be sure that you continue to review your entries, looking closely at yourself and key people in your life. As mentioned in the last chapter, who we are with, and what we are thinking and feeling are all important ingredients in understanding ourselves and our feelings. Look at your entries. Are you munching every time you're angry or feel frustrated? Is it every time you feel hurt, guilty, sad? Look for any feelings which occur repeatedly. Perhaps even more significantly, be suspicious of any feelings which you never seem to have at all

I Always Start . . . .

suspicious of any feelings which you never seem to have at all
– most commonly, anger, hurt and jealousy.

"Okay," you may be thinking. "I understand and agree that
I may be having certain uncomfortable feelings that are not
addressed which may cause me to use food inappropriately. So
what? Understanding does not always stop me from eating!"

I agree. Understanding, awareness, and insight are the
beginning steps in change. You need more. You need some
healthy replacements for eating. Food does work to help
uncomfortable feelings disappear, temporarily. It is a coping
mechanism for discomfort, but food and eating does not
resolve your problems. Food does not make a spouse more
loving, a job more fulfilling, or childhood memories more
pleasant. Food just makes the moment more bearable, but only
for the moment. Choosing to no longer anesthetize these
feeling with food leaves the question of how are you going to
deal with the discomfort. I'm going to show you.

Behind every feeling we experience lies an emotional
need. Learning to directly honor and fulfill these emotional
needs without food is the task at hand. As you learn how to
identify your feelings, recognize the needs that they trigger,
and satisfy these needs in healthy ways, you'll be on your way
to emotionally detaching yourself from food, and permanently
attaching yourself to you.

I'm going to go over a variety of common feelings. As I
discuss each feeling and the need it beckons, I will offer some
very concrete, healthy alternatives. Some of my suggestions
may seem unusual. I encourage you to try what I present.
Whatever my ideas, they will be healthier than eating three
bags of cookies. In the long run, you'll also feel better.

The more you can learn to satisfy your emotional needs in
direct, nurturing ways, the less you'll desire large quantities of
food.

The three most common precipitators for the urge to overeat are:

- ■Anger
- ■Hurt
- ■Boredom

These will be the first three feelings that I will discuss, and begin to divulge how all feelings can be dealt with and eased without using unhealthy vices. Remember, my suggestions will act as a coping mechanism, just as food often does. If you practice my coping mechanisms you'll feel better about yourself and your discomfort will be eased. These suggestions, as with eating, will not resolve your life issues. However, as you start to feel better about yourself, you will possess a new inner strength. It is this new inner strength that will enable you to examine, resolve, and attend to the issues in your life that need attention. There are no miracles or quick fixes. Again, learning about yourself takes time, patience, commitment and love.

Before I begin to discuss healthy replacements for dealing with anger, hurt, boredom, and a variety of other feelings, let me explain how these alternatives assist you in dealing directly with feelings.

The first reason these options work is that they allow you to finally feel in CONTROL of your emotions. When you give yourself permission to identify and feel your feelings directly, without judgement or guilt, a "take charge" feeling emerges. When you can say to yourself, "I have anger, hurt, or loneliness, and I am okay. I know how to deal with these feelings," you will feel an overwhelming sense of being in charge of yourself.

I Always Start . . . .

Many of my clients have shared their feelings of frustration of being out of control unless they're being good on their diet. They focus attention on their food intake rather than on their lives. Working on accepting yourself and the variety of feelings you experience throughout life, taking affirmative action on how to react to these feelings, will allow you to de-emphasize the entire "food/weight" issue.

Instead of emotions controlling you, you're now in control. By controlling them I don't mean pushing them away, or denying them. You are feeling more in control of feelings by allowing them to surface, understanding why you are having these feelings and then making a healthy decision about how to deal with these feelings. The key word here is you, choosing how you need to deal with your emotions. Through this process, feeling in control becomes a familiar state of being.

The second reason that doing the healthy replacements option works is that the suggestions I will be offering will allow you to feel the INTENSITY of the feeling. Most people who use food for emotional reasons are afraid to experience their feelings – especially the feelings that previously have been judged and criticized as being wrong.

Doing some of the replacements allows you to experience the feeling in a non-threatening manner. Once the previously feared feelings are consistently experienced in a safe place, the feeling is no longer perceived as so threatening or scary. The more comfortable you become with experiencing these feelings, the more manageable they are. The situations or thoughts that trigger the feelings may not disappear, but, the intensity will.

The final reason that doing these replacements is important, is that they tend to have a "TRIGGERING" effect. Once you start doing a specific exercise for one particular feeling or situation, it's common for another situation or thought to come to mind. Doing one activity triggers other feelings that may have stayed suppressed. Remember – you have been hiding feelings for years. Keeping things buried comes naturally. By doing these alternatives, suppressed emotions, ones you may have been festering, are brought to the surface. Instead of eating them, you can deal with them.

No matter how silly some of my ideas may sound, please try them. They are no less foolish than eating five bags of cookies, or three pints of ice cream. They are certainly a lot less fattening.

ANGER

Let's begin with anger. Many people have difficulty acknowledging and expressing anger. This difficulty is often due to ingrained beliefs about how "awful" it is to experience and express anger. These teachings, as already discussed, generally come from home and society.

A well-bred, refined, polite sophisticated lady or gentleman does not display angry feelings. If, on the rare occasion, the unmentionable occurs (anger surfaces with a loud voice!), such an individual would work very diligently to cover up these feelings. Anger for many people is so unthinkable and inappropriate to express, that running to the pantry feels like a better solution. Ironically, when someone is eating out of anger, it's usually done in a voracious manner, certainly not politely or with refinement. The biting, chewing, chomping, and the urgency are all done at record breaking speed. Upon completion, anger is released. Unfortunately, extra pounds are added, and the original issues are suppressed.

At last, anger, for all of us, is an inevitable reality. It's one of those emotions, like it or not, that every human being experiences. For this reason, we need to learn how to deal with rage in appropriate ways. Fury is a basic human reaction to an experience that hampers us from achieving a particular goal. This goal can be anything. If you want to go from point A to point B, but there is a large truck in the way, you will probably feel quite perturbed. If you want to date someone special, and that person is not available, most likely, you will feel frustrated. If you want a new job, and cannot find one, you will, inevitably, feel upset. The list of things and events that stir up angry feelings could go on and on infinitely.

Most of us don't get what we want all of the time, so anger will assuredly pop up every now and then. So, what do we need when we are feeling angry? One thing we don't need is to hold it in, and eat. What we do need is to ventilate. We need to release it. We need to get it out. How do we do this venting? I recommend hitting. No, not our loved ones or co-workers, although sometimes that may feel like a good option. Instead, I suggest that you purchase a plastic Whiffle bat. When angry feelings begin to surface, go into a different room and hit your bed, your pillow, a punching bag, the floor, or whatever, as long as it's not valuable, or a person. If you do not want to buy a bat, you can use a towel, and hit it against your bathroom tile. This makes a loud noise! The point is to let your feelings out. Hitting your bed, pillow, punching bag, floor, tile, and screaming while doing it, does not hurt anyone. Rather, it will help you.

I know that this may sound silly, but it works. What I mean by "work" is that venting allows you to feel the intensity of your feelings. It often triggers other feelings, and helps you to feel in control of your emotions. No matter how ridiculous this behavior sounds or feels, please continue to do it. Of course there may be times when you're in touch with your anger. On these occasions, it's not necessary to get up and hit or scream – though you may, especially if you're having an urge to eat. Obviously, at a party or at work, if someone's extremely rude, you can't excuse yourself and go into the other room and start hitting. However, entering the kitchen, though an easier choice, should also be avoided!

You can always leave a room and go to your car and hit the steering wheel, and yell. You can leave the room and write in your journal, too. No editing! It's okay to use strong language in your writing. You can keep a hard rubber ball in your purse or jacket and squeeze it, if need be. You can pull a friend to the side and vent to him/her. The bottom line is that there is always something available to help you address and deal with your feelings, besides the buffet table, candy machine, kitchen, or the nearest super market.

● ● ●

No matter how silly some of my ideas may sound, please try them. They are no less foolish than eating five bags of cookies, or three pints of ice cream. They are certainly a lot less fattening.

● ● ●

All of the aforementioned are healthier ways to deal with anger. They should make you feel better for the moment, as food does. Similarly, they will not resolve the issue. Unlike food, however, they will make you feel better about yourself.

You may have noticed that I did not recommend the

option of confronting the person who triggered your anger. The reason is very important. I have found that is very difficult for many of the people that I have counseled to deal with conflict. Until you can be direct, honest, and comfortable with your feelings of anger, I think it's very difficult to deal with someone else's.

Paula, mother of five-year-old triplets, comes to mind. During the first few years of parenting, her mom, with whom she'd always been close, came over every Monday and Thursday. She helped with the laundry and babysitting. During those early years, Paula was very appreciative. But with the kids in kindergarden, Paula found herself feeling obligated to be with her mom. She no longer needed her at the house. What she needed was peace and quiet and some time alone. Since she didn't want to upset her mom with her own feelings of annoyance, she suppressed them and ate.

Throughout our work, she vented her anger to me and together we worked out a way she could communicate her need for more privacy without nastiness, guilt or hurting her mom. But this took time. So be patient with your feelings.

At this stage of your growth, the first person you need to share your feelings with is you. As mentioned earlier, this is not the 1970s when so many self-help books emphasized the importance of assertiveness-training.

Certainly there is nothing wrong with sharing important feelings with significant others. However, at this particular stage of your growth, it's important to use caution. I know that for myself, I have what I call a 24 hour rule. When I'm sure that someone important to me has done something upsetting to me, I give myself 24 hours to process it. If it's still bothering me the next day, then I decide how I want to approach the situation in a way that will feel comfortable. Ultimately, this may be how you choose to handle conflict. However, you may choose a different path. For now, be careful with how and when you choose to share. The first person you need to share with right now is *you.*

If you are still skeptical about hitting, try this experiment.

List the following five polar traits on a sheet of paper.

Dead-Alive
Ugly-Attractive
Dumb-Smart
Not sexy-Sexy
Fuzzy-Clear

Before you begin hitting your pillow or bed, rate yourself on a scale of 1-10, on how you are feeling right now. For example, if I were to ask you how alive you feel right now, and you felt "blah," you might answer with a "2." Let us say that you are feeling in between, your response might be a "5." Now do this for each pair of adjectives. Then go hit. I mean really let loose for sixty seconds. Now, re-rate yourself.

When I have done this with clients, it always amazes me how their numbers differ. Almost always, their numbers elevate, as do their feelings about themselves. There is a direct correlation between hitting (dealing directly with your feelings) and your self-image. It feels good after hitting, as opposed to the feelings after bingeing.

Healthy replacements allow us to feel our feelings and get on with our day. Dealing with our inner feelings in this new and healthy manner enables us to be more attuned with our messages from inside, those gut feelings to which I keep referring. The more we can get in touch with these powerful, guiding feelings, and are able to listen and follow their messages, the better and more alive we feel. This gut instinct is there for us as a wonderful guide. When followed, we feel enlivened and right. When we do not, we eat.

HURT

Let's go on to another commonly troublesome feeling that often contributes to overeating – hurt. Feeling hurt is not a pleasant experience. Like all feelings, it's one that we are inevitably going to experience. People do things that disappoint us and leave us feeling an empty pain deep in our mid-section. What makes dealing with hurt so difficult is that it's almost always the people we love and who love us that do this hurting. As we are feeling hurt, we are also trying to understand why this loved one hurt us.

It is rare that our loved ones hurt us intentionally. I have never heard a parent say, "I can't wait to hurt my child emotionally." Yet friends and relatives do hurtful things. The first step in dealing with hurt is to accept that you are entitled to your feelings. Suppressing them, or rationalizing them away with such comments as, "Well, they didn't mean it" is not honoring yourself and your emotions. You are always entitled to your feelings.

The second step, after accepting your feelings are justified, is to acknowledge that you need something to make you feel better. Not a large chocolate milk shake! We need the same things a child needs when they're hurting, some comfort. Usually, a good old fashioned hug, and loving words will do the trick. This is what we need, too – a hug with some nurturing words.

When young children are feeling sad or hurt, they innately want to go to their parents for cuddling. However, if their parents are not around, they will go for their blanket or teddy bear, and hold it close. Shortly after, they feel better. They have acknowledged their feelings, and comforted themselves in a healthy manner. This is what you need to do too.

Am I suggesting that you hug and talk to a teddy bear? If there aren't adults around for the job, then yes, that's what I recommend. If you do not have a favorite stuffed animal, go out and buy one. When you notice an urge to eat, and you're pretty certain that is has to do with feeling hurt, bring out your teddy bear, and go into a private place and hug and talk to your bear. Tell your teddy bear how sad and hurt you feel. Switch roles and pretend that your teddy is talking to and comforting you. Be open with your feelings.

This may sound silly or childish, but what about eating an

entire bag of pretzels? Will hugging and speaking with a stuffed animal make your hurt feelings or hurtful person disappear? No, but it will make you feel better temporarily, just as food has done, but without the negative side effects.

● ● ●

Healthy replacements allow us to feel our feelings and get on with our day.

● ● ●

Comforting yourself in this healthy manner will give you a sense of calm and self-compassion, which many of my clients lack. We are wonderfully compassionate, and giving to everyone else's emotional turmoil, but we are less compassionate to ourselves. As you become kinder to yourself, your ability to deal with the event and the individual will increase.

Instead of feeling sad and hurt over our weight and eating habits, which, as already stated, are easier and safer to address than life and relationships, we become more able to deal with the more important aspects of our lives. Feeling sad and empty over poor finances, an awful marriage, and problematic children are all more difficult to resolve than deciding which new diet plan to begin. However, it is ignoring these crucial issues that keep food and weight such an integral part of our self-worth.

Kate, a client of mine, comes to mind. I had seen her several times. She was keeping her journal regularly. At one of our sessions, she relayed the following experience: It was October. Kate, her husband, and two children, ages two and five, decided to go apple picking. She was looking forward to a pleasant afternoon. By the time they were in the car, Kate found herself obsessing about an apple turnover. She was adding up her calorie count for the day. She was figuring out

I Always Start . . . .

how to have one and still feel okay. After several obsessive minutes of apple turnover thoughts, she began pondering why this food item suddenly so imperative to ingest. She had never even had one before. She did decide not to buy one, but Kate's craving continued and feelings of deprivation remained.

Through our work together, she was already aware that whether she bought the turnover or not was not the key issue. What was significant was the all-encompassing desire, and the tremendous feeling of denial and deprivation. When she arrived home, she wrote in her journal. She realized what she was more feeling deprived of was a supportive, emotionally intimate husband. Although her husband was willing to go on this outing, he complained several times about missing the football game. He also was not very helpful when their two-year-old son became crabby. She felt alone the entire day.

As Kate wrote, she became aware of her true inner sadness, hurt, and emptiness. Though unpleasant feelings, they are real, and through facing them, her desire for the apple turnover disappeared. It was a non-issue. What she did instead was grab her teddy bear and use it as a comforter. She then knew that she needed to discuss her feelings and marital issues with me. As she became clearer of her issues, she brought her husband in for marital therapy. She chose to share her feelings. The more we explored her marriage and her true insides, the more her outside came closer to a comfortable weight.

For Kate, writing, cuddling with a teddy bear, counseling and talking with her husband were all comforting. Still another option is to keep a small tape recorder handy and talk into it when you're feeling hurt. You can call a friend and ask for time to share your feelings with them. Any of these suggestions are reaffirming that your feelings and needs count. Doing these healthy replacements will strengthen your emotional muscles, enabling you to take care of yourself without abusing food, or your body.

Once you start and continue to take care of your emotional needs directly, food will become an enjoyable, delicious, and healthy *part* of your life instead of being a feared entity. When you allow yourself to feel and accept your hurt, you'll recognize the need for comfort and that excessive intake of food is no longer a viable option for self-consolation.

BOREDOM

I can't count the times I've heard from my clients that they eat from boredom. Their comments sound something like, "There's nothing to do. I hate just hanging around the house doing nothing. I don't know what to do, so eating is what I do."

The issue is deeper than simple boredom. The cycle looks more like this: you have time on your hands, and you're not sure what to do. You could clean the closets, pay some bills, or do some paper work from the office. However, none of these activities really feel "right," so you do nothing. You want something fun, exciting, stimulating, or something with which to busy yourself. When you have nothing to do on the outside, it's very common to begin looking on the inside. Questions begin to surface. "Why is everything so boring? How come I have nothing to do? I should be doing the closets, but I'm too lazy! Why can't I find anything appealing to consume myself with? What's wrong with me?" Somewhere around these last few questions would be the time food would start its seduction.

Being unable to be comfortable with yourself without a scheduled, productive activity often triggers feelings of inadequacy and uncertainty, and eating helps to avoid these feelings. I'm not saying there is anything wrong with keeping busy and finding productive activities. If having some projects around makes your feel good, then by all means do them. Some quick suggestions include a favorite author's latest novel set aside for a rainy day, going to the library or video store, reading *People* magazine or *Time*, or taking a walk or bike ride. Any of these activities, when planned ahead, are what I call "preventative medicine" self-care. You know yourself well enough to know when you're busy and fulfilled, you feel better about yourself – therefore, less likely to turn to food.

● ● ●

Once you...take care of your emotional needs directly, food will become an enjoyable, delicious, and healthy *part* of your life instead of being a feared entity.

● ● ●

However, not every moment in our lives is perfectly planned and productive. If you're in a situation where you cannot do a designated activity, and you are not really in the mood to clean the closets, you can use this time to be with yourself. Put on some classical music, or whatever your pleasure, and just be with self. Think, write, and meditate. Use this time to become more attuned with your inner self, and your inner feelings. Try and be compassionate and complimentary to yourself. Make a list of at least five qualities that you like about yourself.

The goal is to begin building a solid and healthy relationship with self. You are a unique and interesting human being, hardly boring! Boring is another word for self-hate.

When you love being with yourself for the day, you won't need to run from yourself into the kitchen. It is okay to NOT always be productive. Where does that message/value come from that 24 hours daily of business and productivity are essential for good self esteem? Challenge old messages/values until you figure out what feels right for you.

This week, continue your journaling, but also include taking five minutes each day to hit, hug, and be with yourself. As you do these exercises, you should notice a reduction in your eating urges. Identifying your feelings, realizing that these feelings have needs, and satisfying these needs are the three steps that, if regularly executed, will lead you down the path to self-fulfillment and a body weight that you can accept with a smile, both on the inside and the outside.

I hope you've have designated your five minutes each day to include a hit, a hug, and of course, your journal. As previously mentioned, if, after doing the suggested activities, new, powerful feelings surface, seek out a competent therapist for assistance. Sometimes new feelings can be overwhelming. A caring professional can be extremely helpful in this changing process. Knowing, and seeking out assistance is another healthy self-help step on the journey to appropriate eating, and to an improved self-image.

Chapter Seven
More Feelings, More Replacements

Let's move on to some other feelings that often precipitate the urge to overeat. I will also recommend more replacements, other than food, to address these feelings.

GUILT

After anger, hurt, and boredom, guilt is right up there as an extremely common emotion to elicit that all-encompassing urge for food. Guilt is a problem because of its nature. Unlike anger, hurt, and boredom, guilt is derived from inner value conflicts. It's usually about something we did, or did not do, that we not only regret, but makes us feel like we are a "bad" person. Guilt can hang in there like the tenacity of a bill collector, always looking for another payment. It hangs in there so strongly because we feel so deeply that we have violated a significant value. We truly believe that we have done something vile.

Trying to figure out what we need when we are feeling guilty is more complex than hitting or hugging. However, the answer is still not food. Understanding guilt means addressing, assessing, and perhaps changing some of your values.

For example, when my mother entered parenthood, staying home with the children was seen as the appropriate "good" thing to do. Every day at lunch, she was home with a well-balanced meal, and hugs and kisses. Mothers of that era who were not home to give this nutritious lunch and love package were looked down upon. They were even ostracized by other "decent" mothers. Those mothers that did work either for financial reason, or heaven for bid, for their mental welfare, felt the wrath of their peers. They suffered from large doses of guilt.

Today, this has shifted. Perhaps this shift may be too far

on the other end of the spectrum. Now, if you "only" stay home with kids, and are not career bound, you would be frowned upon. Though working women and many others say staying home in and of itself is a full day's work and it's wonderful if you stay home, many women feel this is not enough – especially true among older moms who worked before having children.

So staying home today can produce the same intensity of guilt that thirty years ago brought accolades. With guilt then, it's not so much the actual circumstance or situation; rather, it's our *interpretation* and belief system about the event.

Since guilt is about our beliefs, we need to reexamine them. For example, a client of mine named Roxie was invited to a wedding. Roxie lives in the suburbs of Chicago, and the wedding was at a hotel in the heart of the city. She decided that she would surprise her husband and get a room in the hotel and stay overnight. During the week before the wedding, she received a phone call from a neighbor, who was also invited to the wedding. Her neighbor is divorced, and does not like to drive at night. She asked Roxie for a ride to and from the wedding. Roxie likes her neighbor, and feels sorry for her. Her divorce was messy, and she has a lot of health problems. Roxie knew that she wanted to say "no," but felt that she would be a terrible person if she did not give this lady a ride. She told her neighbor that she would get back to her.

For the next two hours, Roxie nibbled, going back and forth to the pantry until she contacted me. We began exploring why Roxie felt it was her responsibility to take care of this neighbor. It's wonderful that she wants to be helpful, and as our dialogue continued, she shared with me that she frequently assists this lady – but how this neighbor got to this wedding was not her only job in life. We discussed her family, and how her mother drummed into her head how you must be nice to everyone, all of the time. Roxie's needs were never important. Everyone else's feelings came first.

I suggested that she had every right to have a nice evening

with her husband. If she wanted to be helpful to her neighbor, then Roxie could make some additional calls to assist her in finding her neighbor a ride, or mention that a cab is always an option. The bottom line really was: could Roxie be comfortable with saying "no" when her needs were challenged?

This is a typical example of guilt. We all have certain rules, values, and beliefs, defining the "right" way to live. I'm suggesting that there really is no right or wrong, other than the basic golden rule approach. Even this rule states, "Do unto others as you would do to yourself." Guilt is about labeling and judging our personhood. If I'm angry at my mother and hang up on her, I may not be pleased with my behavior, but it does not mean that I'm a terrible person. A h e l p f u l intervention in dealing with guilt is to do what I just described. We all do or say we later regret. However, instead of honing in on our entire selfhood, lets just focus on the behavior and relabel guilt with the word "remorse." Remorse is a healthy feeling that encourages us to behave in ways we admire. As I just said, none of us is perfect, and at times we occasionally behave in ways that later need reassessment. Using the word remorse, and focusing on the behavior discourages moral judgements that often lead to self-name bashing. If I feel badly that I was rude to my mom, I can call myself a bunch of horrible names and feel like a piece of dirt, eat, or I can give myself time to reflect on my actions and then choose how I want to rectify the situation. I can call my mom and apologize, I can send a card or flowers, I can take her for lunch, or whatever. I may even decide that she deserved it and say nothing. Whatever is decided, the attention is placed on the situation, not your character. It's much easier to resolve a situation than to alter your entire personhood.

I Always Start . . . .

To deal with guilt – without food – you need to do the following three things:

- Reevaluate your own values. Check out your "should" statements. You do not have to follow and abide by the same values with which you were raised.
- Relabel guilty feelings using the word remorse. Address the situation, not your moral character.
- Develop a plan of action to deal with the presenting situation.

Doing all three exercises will increase your odds of weight stabilization, and even weight loss.

WORRY

The counterpart to guilt is worry. Whereas guilt or remorse is about something we feel we have done inappropriately in the past, worry is a concern of what may or may not be in the future. We may worry about money, friends, children, parents, career, marriage, and of course, weight.

There is nothing unusual about having healthy concerns for important areas in our lives. The key phrase is "healthy concern." Many of the people that I have dealt with obsess about what their future may or may not hold. The problem is none of us know for sure what the future will bring. Part of being emotionally healthy is accepting this often frustrating part of life and understanding that if we are not immediately granted a particular desire, maybe we need to ask ourselves why, and move and grow from there.

Nancy is a single woman who is having difficulty dealing with the fact that she is unwed. Although she is a very successful business woman with many friends and a warm family, more than anything, she desires a family of her own. She is attractive, bright, and has a lively sense of humor. She has dated many men, but has not found the right one. Her biological clock is ticking, yet she does not want to settle as did many of her friends. If she is home on a Saturday night, she finds herself consumed with thoughts of loneliness and sadness. She ruminates over the next five years. If not married by then, children will no longer be an option. Her pain is clear, and she turns to food. What might be a better alternative to deal with her pain?

I began by working with the concept that the present is really all any of us have for sure. By finding ways to enjoy today, fulfilling our lives with interesting and stimulating people and experiences. By focusing our attentions to our inner self and growth, we have less time and energy to focus on what we do not have in our lives. No one's life is perfect. Everyone has something or some desire that is not forthcoming with which to contend. But when we are kind to ourselves and ensure our emotional, intellectual, spiritual, and physical needs are attended to, what may be currently unavailable has less importance. In fact, often, with patience and introspection, we may learn that what we thought we wanted so desperately is in fact not what we really desired at all.

This is not to say Nancy did not want marriage and a family. I'm sure she did. Instead of sitting home and focusing so much of her attention on the lack of marriage and family, I encouraged her to examine how much she has achieved as a single woman. I pushed her to see how, as a single person, she could explore her own interests and develop her inner self. As she began moving away from what she did not have, which is a waste of time for all of us, and moved toward what she did have and could continue having, her progress was more than evident. Her eating stabilized, her self-image improved, her interests expanded. Her ability to derive joy from self, close friends, and family increased. Ironically enough, as she put less emphasis on her husband and family, she met a very nice man with whom she is currently quite serious.

With all the feelings that you experience, the more you're able to understand them, see them as doorways to self-learning, and fulfill the needs they conjure up, not only will your weight be less of an issue, but your self-esteem will soar upward. You may not meet Mr. or Ms. Right, you may not win the lottery or have perfect kids, but the good news is, these desires will no longer carry the same weight...physically, or emotionally.

TENSION

Another common feeling that often causes inappropriate food usage is tension. In today's world, we are all bombarded with so many outside stimuli that it's no wonder we feel stressed and full of tension. When we feel tense what do we need? The answer is relaxation. What does relaxation look like? For each of us, the answer is different. Eating is certainly one option. I think that there are healthier choices. Before discussing these other choices, it is imperative to address your feelings about the RIGHT kind of relaxation.

I find myself thinking about Barbara. Barbara is 38 years old. She is married, and has two daughters, ages five and seven. She works full time as an accountant. She also is a room mother and deacon at her church. Her husband works nights, and is not available to really help with the kids in the evening.

Most commonly, Barbara eats at night. As we began exploring her day, and how tense she felt, she began to cry. She shared how overwhelmed she felt, and how she had no time for herself. As I began offering suggestions about how she might be able to make some time for herself, she responded with many "Yes, but..." I asked her if she felt that she really deserved some relaxation time. She was hesitant, and answered, "I would feel lazy, like I wasn't using my time productively." To Barbara, relaxing felt bad. Even though, intellectually, she knew that she desperately needed some time off, emotionally, she felt it was wrong.

This is a common phenomenon in people who overeat. As mentioned earlier, many overeaters are perfectionists, raised in families where they're taught to constantly give. Giving to self is seen as selfish and wrong. These messages need to be strongly challenged and changed. As I have stated throughout this book, self-care is an essential ingredient in permanent change.

When feeling tense, the first step is to stop and reevaluate how you feel about relaxation. Relaxation is mandatory for a fulfilling life. Relaxation can be in the form of a planned bubble bath each evening. It can be setting aside time to read a trashy novel, a magazine, playing solitaire, knitting, sewing, listening to music, watching sitcoms, talking on the phone, meditating, writing in your journal, getting a massage, or playing a sport. The point is to validate your need for some time off, and to find a way to set aside time for relaxation. You should never feel you don't deserve it.

One other helpful suggestion when feeling tense or stressed is to try reinterpreting the actual situation that may be causing you tension. I recently did a cable show on stress. After taping for several hours, we realized that there was no sound. I was not happy! I knew that we had to re-shoot, so I calmed myself down, and then had an idea to do the show in a different format.

• • •

Self-care is an essential ingredient in permanent change.

• • •

The second taping actually went better than the first. Reinterpreting a tense situation, looking at options, and having faith in yourself can turn a tense situation into a positive one.

Becoming aware that there is stress in your life is the beginning step to change. You must go ahead and do something that will help the tension lessen. We all have many important responsibilities. However, our emotional needs are important as well. If you do not balance enjoyment and responsibilities, the cost is high, not only on the scale, but also around the ones we love. If you want to stop using food, take the time to take care of your need to relax. Whether a bath, a book, or a reinterpretation of an event, the more you can do to feel relaxed, the less you'll need ice cream.

FEELING TRAPPED

Another troublesome feeling is that of being trapped. Feeling that you are in a situation with no way out is extremely uncomfortable. This can be in an unsatisfying job, relationship, or a difficult financial circumstance. When feeling trapped, most of us want a way out in order to feel liberated. We want to feel less confined and more independent.

How we achieve this liberated feeling often seems impossible. Usually we are aware that a job is not going to change, nor is the other person in the uncomfortable relationship, and we are probably not going to win the lottery to rectify our finances. Eating will not resolve any of these situations. The solution resides in our ability to look inside ourselves and change.

For example, let's say that you're going to visit your parents in Florida. You only see them twice a year, and as they're getting on in years, you want to make the best of each visit. Unfortunately, though they mean well, they're often quite critical, and make you feel terrible.

Each time you're with them, you hope that they will be nicer, more supportive. But alas, by day two of the visit they begin their "comments." It may be about your weight, your job, your friends or your clothes. You feel hurt, angry, and trapped. Where can you go? Should you vow never to visit them? How can you be with them and feel free to be yourself?

The answers are not easy. You are certain that running away and never seeing them again will not feel any better than being with them. My answer to the last question is, "Yes, you can be with them and be yourself, however, with a qualification. While validating and understanding that your trapped feelings are real, you need to come to terms with the fact that your parents are not going to change. You need to change your expectations. This is very important. Once you change your expectations, you can plan a better self-care, liberating strategy for your visits."

Perhaps, instead of staying for a week, you can keep your visits to a long week-end. During these visits, you should plan some outside excursions. You will have some benign topics of conversation ready to go when the "comments" begin, because they will begin. You may be thinking, "Why not just tell them to be quiet? Their comments are hurtful." This certainly can be tried, but be aware while they may step back for a while, within a short period, the comments will return. Most parents just can't help themselves. Their need to be "helpful" overrides their child's feelings and needs. It is usually wiser to look inside yourself for change, especially if your parents are elderly.

This same process may be used when dealing with any situation where you feel trapped. In a job situation, look at how you can make things feel better. If you know that you cannot leave right now, look at the company's benefits. If your company covers dental work and you need some done, now might be a good time to book the procedure. If you have several sick days coming, take them, using this time for job searching. If there is anyone with whom you work that you would like to know better, make lunch plans. Anything you can do to make a situation more tolerable, other than snacking, will ensure that trapped feelings will flee.

Remember, with all of our feelings, including feelings of being trapped, we need to consistently remind ourselves that our feeling state is valid. You are allowed to feel the way you do, any time.

What is important is what we do with these feelings, and how we fulfill the needs that they trigger. If you really get stuck and are unsure of what to do, ask a friend for help. Asking for help is not a weakness, but a strength. Brainstorming with a friend can be highly productive as well as fun. The more liberated you feel, the less likely you are, emotionally, to abuse food and yourself.

FEELING UNATTRACTIVE

Another common feeling that can bring on an eating episode is feeling unattractive. This feeling usually starts as soon as we awake. We look in the mirror and start focusing on the physical part of us which we hate the most. The criticism begins. As our self-flagellation continues, we feel worse and worse. We may just throw on anything to cover ourselves. We may feel so awful that we don't put on our make up or do our hair. By the time we reach the kitchen, a big breakfast seems quite alluring.

A big breakfast will not increase the chances of feeling better about yourself, or your appearance. I have spent the majority of this book encouraging you to look inside yourself, where the true answers to good self-worth reside; but to totally ignore your appearance seems extreme. Of course, putting time and energy into your hair, make up, clothes or nails will not resolve your life problems either. But this effort will cause you to continually make statements to yourself such as, "I am important. I deserve – no matter what the scale reads – to take care of my physical appearance."

This is often a difficult commitment to make to yourself. If you agree that it is who we are on the inside that really counts, then why bother with the outside? Because our souls are housed in our physical bodies, and our bodies need to be taken care of and respected. The same is true with our intellect and emotions.

Change is inclusive, not exclusive. This means that we need to address all of our needs. Taking care or your appearance is not selfish or superficial, unless you are looking in the mirror 24 hours a day. I am talking about balance, and will be talking more about body image in Chapter 9. You do not need to spend several hours grooming yourself. Look at yourself and your schedule. Figure out what feels doable and then do it. If you need to get up ten minutes earlier to wash your hair, you are worth it. The key here is accepting that this self-care is worthwhile, and figuring out what will work best for you. Spending a little extra time on personal appearance, although not the end-all and be-all of problem solving, is self-loving and self-nourishing, much more so than doughnuts.

INADEQUACY

There are many emotions that can contribute to turning to food. I have chosen the ones that I have found to be the most common. There are certainly many more. The one that is intertwined with all of them are feelings of inadequacy.

Feelings of inadequacy usually stem from childhood. Many people with low self-esteem had parents who were highly critical. Whatever we did or did not do was judged. How we felt was not considered; rather it was put down. Name calling was common. Differentiation was viewed as mutiny. Families were to be cohesive, and follow very clearly stated rules of behavior, and acceptable personality traits. Dysfunction was generally high.

I find myself thinking of Cindy, a 26 year old, the third of five children. Her father is a very successful businessman, and her mother is a homemaker. Her father has always been a leader in the community, and at home. He had very strict rules about everything. All five kids had to do things his way. This was a problem for Cindy, who was very sensitive and remains so. She is very artistic and loves children. Growing up, she loved playing house and doing art projects with her friends. Her father found this "babyish" and "wasteful." When her older brother teased her, Cindy would begin to cry. Her father would place her in the corner with a dunce cap, calling her a cry baby.

At school, although she did fine, concentrating was always

difficult for her. She would complain to her mom, asking for her help, but her mom, too, was scared of dad's rules. His children "should" always do well in school. Cindy had nowhere to turn. Her dad was awful, and her mom was too scared to help. Cindy became bulimic. For eight years she ate and vomited almost every day. Her eating behavior disgusted her, deepening her feelings of inadequacy.

Through our sessions together, she began to see that she was not such an awful person. Cindy had managed to graduate college, and was working as an art teacher. She enjoyed her work and received good feedback from the children and her peers. As she began understanding her parents' dysfunction, she was able to let go of their distorted and incorrect view of her; and as she began understanding her parents' dysfunction, Cindy was able to let go of expecting their approval, beginning to see the inner lovely, bright, sensitive young woman she was.

What we need when we feel inadequate is a reality check. I have worked with hundreds of people who have eating/weight issues. Each person I have met has been a pleasure to know. I have found them to be introspective, caring, bright, loving, fun...I could go on and on. The only problem was that, I, along with their friends, saw these qualities clearly, but they did not. They had taken on the same critical, judgmental opinions they'd been brainwashed to believe. In my work, I sometimes feel as though I am a de-programmer. The way they see themselves – and perhaps the way you see yourself – is not real.

The more you can accept that, although you may not be perfect, you are a wonderful, unique, human being. Upon making an error, instead of berating yourself, try to forgive and be as compassionate and loving to yourself as you would be to friends. If friends forgot to call when they said they would, I doubt you would call them incompetent, forgetful jerks, but this is just how you may treat yourself.

Calling friends and asking what they like about you can be

a first step in seeing yourself more clearly. Or put an empty chair across from you and ask it what you are feeling about yourself. Then move to the chair and play therapist to yourself. See if you can be empathic and comforting. Or, if your feelings of inadequacy are very overwhelming, see a professional therapist. To continually label yourself as inadequate for everything you do or say is unrealistic and untruthful. On the basics of probability alone, no one can be that bad all of the time, and you are certainly not.

FINDING THE RIGHT ALTERNATIVES FOR YOU

The feelings which I have presented are the ones I have found to be the most common contributors to people staying emotionally involved with food and weight. As already mentioned, there are dozens more (see page 63-64 for a listing of other common feelings). Your might have noticed that I did not include "happy" feelings as a trigger to overeating. Although there are many people who say they have overeaten when joyful, I tend to dispute this comment. Upon hundreds of interviews, I have found that when people are really having a wonderful time feeling truly joyful, they rarely abuse food. Feeling pure joy is, in itself, a high. This is not to say that while attending a party one might not overindulge just a bit. We all have had that kind of experience. But if a client of mine came into my office sharing a binge episode that was experienced at a large buffet and swore that everything, emotionally, was wonderfully fine, I would find myself encouraging her to look deeper. Upon further exploration, I feel certain a disquieting, uncomfortable feeling would be uncovered. If you are feeling genuinely good about yourself, food does not beckon.

You will note that I have included two charts on the following pages. One gives you a quick reference guide to dealing with uncomfortable feelings and fulfilling emotional needs without eating. The suggested replacements and alternatives are just that. The other is for you to fill in. Feel free to come up with anything that feels right for you. For feelings that I may have excluded, add them to this chart and see what kind of alternative you can arrive at to deal with the feeling and needs.

For every feeling that you use food to cope with, you can replace eating with a different, more positive soother. These new soothers will meet your emotional needs head on, and allow you to feel much better about yourself.

With continued journaling and self-diagnosis of feelings, you'll be able to continuously come up with your own prescriptions for self-care. Whatever new feelings surface, your validating and honoring approach will allow you to handle these feelings and needs in a mature, healthy manner, without food.

FEELING CHART

Feeling	Need	Replacements
Anger	Ventilation	Hit a pillow, scream and yell, write a letter
Hurt	Comfort	Hug a teddy bear, a pet, a friend
Guilt/remorse	Feeling unguilty/ off the hook	Look at act and find solution; avoid making good/bad judgment
Tension	Relaxation	Bubble bath, massage, music, book, soap operas
Feeling trapped	Feeling freer	Reinterpret situation, take a class, helpless share feelings with a friend
Feeling inadequate	Feeling adequate	Get support from a friend, rational self-talk either silently or into a tape recorder
Feeling unattractive	Feeling attractive	Put on fresh makeup or shave, get a haircut or manicure, change clothes

FEELING CHART

Feeling   **Need**   **Replacements**

FEELING CHART

<u>Feeling</u>   **<u>Need</u>**   **<u>Replacements</u>**

Chapter Eight

Making Sure Your Needs Are Met

I *am hoping you are experiencing some relief* from food's emotional pull. As you are more in touch with your feelings, aware of the needs that they conjure up, and address these needs, food should no longer feel as important. The more you confront your feelings and fears in a compassionate, caring manner, your weight will reach an acceptable level for you, your body, and your self image. Your inner voice and your gut feelings, should be feeling something right now...like, "Yes, this makes sense!" Remember, this gut feeling is there to guide you. Listen to the feeling and you'll always feel alive. When this feeling is ignored, food will beckon.

Part of listening also means taking some action. Journaling is one part of the action that you have already taken. You're more aware of your feelings. Perhaps not every feeling, as this takes time and requires awareness. You may now notice that when you say "Yes" and you mean "No," it's not long after that you are in the kitchen. You may see how "nice" you are to others, and not as nice to yourself. As you're aware of these behaviors and the feelings that are aroused, comforting them begins to finally feel right.

In the previous chapter, replacements were suggested. These replacements for food need to be implemented and expanded to your lifestyle. Issues will continue to arise in your life. These issues will make you feel emotions. These emotions have needs. Making sure that these needs get fulfilled is extremely important in permanently changing your relationship with food and self. Fulfilling your emotional needs is often a difficult part of change.

For example, there was Anne, a 30 year old mother of a two year old. As a school teacher, Anne took a leave of absence to be with her child. Anne really loved to teach, and had not planned on quitting so soon. When she became unexpectedly pregnant, she made the decision to stay home with her daughter. Her husband was doing well financially; Anne did not need to continue to work. However, each afternoon, as her daughter napped, she found herself in the kitchen, grazing from the pantry to the refrigerator. She knew that she was not hungry, but she just kept eating.

As we began exploring her feelings, we discovered that she was feeling unfulfilled and empty by staying home. She grew up in a family where both of her parents worked. Her mother was in real estate, and was often out. Her dad was a corporate executive who traveled a great deal. Anne was taught to value keeping busy and being productive. She learned to take care of herself by keeping busy. She learned to cook dinner, read, or clean her room. This helped to deaccentuate any lonely feelings that she experienced. Staying occupied became fun. Therefore, staying home with a baby, going to the park, and pushing a swing, or being in a moms' and tots' class was boring and unfulfilling for her.

She loved her child, but there was only so much baby talk she could handle. Yet, she felt guilty about having these feelings. She has a healthy child and was financially comfortable, so she "should" be grateful and content. Why, with everything that she had, should she feel so empty?

Anne had rules about how she was supposed to feel. For her mother, being out of the house and working felt right. Anne was similar to her mother; however, she harbored feelings of being alone as a child. She did not want her daughter to feel these feelings of loneliness. Yet if she stayed home, Anne felt that she would go crazy. Her inner voice was screaming to her, "You need more!" Each time this voice shouted, Anne would turn a deaf ear. She was afraid that if she listened, she would return to full-time teaching. To Anne, her choices seemed cut and dried, all or nothing. In her mind, it was either go back to teaching full-time, or stay home with her daughter. Neither choice felt viable. She did not see any other options.

This kind of thinking is common. It feels like a lose-lose situation, but rarely is any life situation a total bust. The first step in resolving the presenting problem, and being able to take the action needed, is to honor the feelings at hand. Anne feels that she needs more stimulation. This is the key issue. She may be around ten other mothers who love staying home, attending play groups, and going to the park. The fact that these other woman are completely fulfilled is wonderful, for them. This is not to say that Anne did not enjoy and love motherhood; she did. However, she, as do many woman, was very busy comparing herself to others. We each have our own special needs. If ours differ from someone else's, that's fine. Be yourself and honor your inner voice and what it says to you.

After you have honored your feelings and the needs that they stir up, you can begin listing some options. For every situation there are usually at least five possibilities. Anne and I began brainstorming. She shared that she had always wanted to go back to school for a Masters Degree in education. She also had an interest in drawing. Sometimes, she just wanted to get out of the house alone and go shopping, or spend an evening alone with her husband. She also loved to write. As we explored these five areas that she felt would lead to intellectual stimulation, and adult dialogue, she began feeling better.

She soon signed up for an evening course and registered for a drawing course where they also had a nursery. Another morning she hired a sitter and just ran errands. Anne and her husband found at least one evening together. When her daughter napped, Anne would write. As she validated her feelings and began fulfilling her emotional needs, her grazing magically diminished. There really was no magic in Anne's stabilized eating. However, it did take some effort. You, too, need to look at your feelings without judgement or criticism. Your feelings are your feelings. Even if others may not feel the way you do. This is perfectly okay. If you realize that you need something more in your life, do what's necessary to ensure that it's met.

You may be thinking, "I have no idea what I need to make me feel better." Or, "I know what I need, and it's a million dollars, or the perfect mate!" To help clarify and make your needs more attainable, it's often helpful to make an uncensored list of your top ten needs. The list would look something like this after you first make sure that you have validated your feelings in a positive mode:

I need more _____ in my life.

1)
2)
3)
4)
5)
6)
7)
8)
9)
10)

Fill in the blanks. Sometimes this is fairly easy. You may already be aware of some things missing in your life. Good. At other times, you may need a bit more thought. That's okay, just do it. Write down whatever comes to your mind. Remember, for every need you jot down, there are probably at least five ways to get that need met in ways other than eating. Anne's list might have looked like this:

I need more _____ in my life.

1) Intellectual stimulation
2) Fun
3) Relaxation
4) Time alone
5) Physical activity
6) Time with friends
7) Time with husband
8) Advanced education
9) Cultural stimulation
10) Exploration of drawing

After you make your list, draw a vertical line down the middle of the paper and jot down how you might begin to meet these needs. Anne's might look like this:

I Always Start . . . .

I need more _____. Here's how I'm going to do it.

1) Intellectual stimulation . . . . Read
2) Fun . . . . Tape and watch soap operas
3) Relaxation . . . . Take a bubble bath
4) Time alone . . . . Get a sitter and go to the
                                     library or mall alone
5) Physical activity . . . . Walk/bike
6) Time with friends . . . . Make lunch plans
7) Time with husband . . . . . . Get sitter two weeks in advance
8) Advanced education . . . . Take a course
9) Cultural stimulation . . . . Monthly museum visit
10) Exploration of drawing . . . . Take an art class

This exercise should help you become more attuned to the needs in your life, and how you can begin fulfilling them. But because our lives can feel so busy and hectic, we may wonder how we are going to find the time to take care of our emotional needs along with everyone else's. Sometimes it seems difficult to consider adding a new dimension to your life. Take a moment to consider the following: How much are you willing to finally begin meeting your inner needs? How willing are you to face the unknown of self-care? As stated in chapter one, change is scary for all of us. Addressing our fears and finding our own inner truth is the prescription for weight control.

If you're journaling and searching for those hidden "missing" feelings, you're on your way. If you're hitting, hugging your teddy bear, reviewing your journal entries, and validating your feelings, you're on the road to change. Another reminder that the real issue is NOT THE FOOD. Food is a way of coping. We eat, giving our emotions and needs a backseat to those of others. The consistent challenge is learning to be self-directed and still considerate of others – difficult, but when achieved, wholly satisfying.

It's important to remember that all people, including our loved ones, have life issues that need their attention. If they're not using food or any other unhealthy vice to deal with them, this is admirable. Herein lies our goal: learning how to cope with life's problems in healthy, self-caring ways. Learning what your needs are, realizing their importance and satisfying them, can make you feel deliciously alive. Your needs are always equally as important as others' around you.

If, after reading this and trying the previous exercise, you're still uncertain of what your needs are, give yourself some time. As I have repeatedly stated, many people keep their feelings and needs repressed. Try to give yourself some thinking time and ask, "If uncensored, what do I really want in my life?" See what kind of answers you feel deep within. Because these responses will probably come from this inner voice, this gut feeling which I have been describing – listen carefully. Your answers might come in the form of words in your head, from a conversation with a friend, from a book, or television. Something will hit you, and just feel right. Even if right now, what you need feels elusive, the answers are inside of you.

● ● ●

Our goal: learning how to cope with life's problems in healthy, self-caring ways.

● ● ●

People have often described an emptiness in their life. We are often not exactly sure why, but it's just a feeling. This emptiness can never be satisfied or filled with food. It can be filled with careful attention to its source, and then giving this emptiness healthy, appropriate nourishment. This nourishment can be school, rest, reading, knitting, hiking, traveling, meditation, or religious services. For each of us, the answer is different and unique.

As you become more adept to figuring out what you emotional needs are, it's important that these needs are regularly nurtured. To help assure that these needs are cared for, I recommend that you fill out the enclosed chart.

I have used the acronym P.U.F., which is pronounced POOF. Everyone is looking for the next magic diet, so here is a little magic chart! P.U.F. stands for Putting "U" First.

Many of us are uncomfortable about taking care of our emotional needs and feel we don't deserve good care; this chart challenges these ridiculous and unhealthy beliefs. As already stated, the better we treat ourselves, the more energy and love we have to give to others. Our anger, resentment, jealousy, and all feelings that have led us to food, dissipate as we learn to be nice to self. Putting "U" First encourages you to take care of yourself first, for the first time in your life. Let's not forget what our flight attendants tell us when traveling with a youngster. Give yourself oxygen first, so you can more easily take care of the child. The more easily we breathe, the more capable we are to assist our kids. This is also true when at home. We do not want to exclude others, but include ourselves.

To use the PUF chart, start by examining your list of needs from the previous exercise. Whatever you have jotted down as possible activities should be noted and graded on a scale from one to ten. One being almost impossible to do, and ten being very feasible. You know your lifestyle, so be creative in ways to increase satisfaction in your life.

After you have completed your list and feel comfortable with it, on another sheet of paper, list your weekly responsibilities. (Yes, we still need to do our responsibilities. If we blow them off, we will feel terrible and possibly turn to food.) Your responsibilities might include work, grocery shopping, car pools, cleaning, meetings or errands. Upon this list's completion, you are ready to fill in your self-care schedule.

The self-care PUF schedule is a chart divided into squares, each representing a specific time of day. First you are to fill in your daily and weekly responsibilities. This can be done at the beginning of the week. As schedules often change, each evening you may need to review the following day's chores, and rearrange them as necessary. After your responsibilities are accounted for, it's equally as important that your emotional needs are affirmed.

Examine your list of needs and how you planned to fulfill them. For example, if on your list your wrote, "I need more relaxation" and that meant a bubble bath, look at your PUF chart and find a time to enjoy a luxury bath. Or let's say you wanted more time with your friends. Get on the phone and book a lunch date. The idea is to validate and honor your needs and then fulfill them in healthy ways. The more you can fill yourself up with emotionally healthy things, the less you'll need food.

Some of you still may be having difficulty figuring out what you need. For so long, food was used as the main filler of emotional needs. To assist those who are still having problems ascertaining what their needs are, try the following exercise. Look through a magazine and choose a picture of someone you would like to look like. Pick a full length photo, preferably not a celebrity. Take your time, and see what you choose. Please select only one picture, before reading on. If you read on the purpose of the exercise will be lost.

Okay, I hope you have your picture. Take out a sheet of paper and divide it in half. On the first half write: "ME NOW." Underneath, describe yourself, what you are like today. Include both physical attributes and personality characteristics. Take a picture from a magazine, carefully studying the photo. On the second half of the paper write: "THE PICTURE." Describe her as fully as you can, including her appearance as well as what personality traits you see.

I Always Start . . . .

Let's see how this worked for Sherri. She picked a very dynamic looking woman. The adjectives she used in her description included: sexy, attractive, voluptuous, energetic, flashy, successful, independent, hard, married, has a career, a go getter. She then compared the adjective to the ones she used to describe herself. They were: soft, plain, sincere, bright, loving, sensitive, nice, comfortable to be with, a caretaker. Look at the difference between the two descriptions!

There are hundreds of pictures to choose from. It's not a coincidence that you picked the one you did. This picture tells something about what's missing in your life. In Sherri's case, her picture represented someone who "had it all." Granted, the woman that she picked might have been too extreme, but it represented the image that Sherri wanted. Your picture, too, will give you some ideas of what you may want and need in your life.

When I have done this exercise with clients, I am often surprised by their choices. I will never forget Rita, a twenty-five year old accountant who always came in after work wearing a blue suit with a white blouse. She wore no make up, and was very conservative. She brought in a picture of a woman in sexy lingerie. It was an extremely provocative ad. As we explored why she chose this particular picture, she shared some views about her sexuality. She was very shy, and never really felt comfortable about her body and sex. It was clear that this was an area that she needed to explore. As a beginning step, I encouraged her to block off time in her PUF chart for shopping at Victoria's Secret!

The point is to try and discover what your needs are, and to try and find ways to meet them – without using food. Another client brought in a picture of a skier; she needed more physical activity in her life. Yet another brought in a picture of someone on the beach. She needed a vacation. Everyone has a variety of needs, whether it's relaxation, creativity, feeling loved, having fun, or needing some adventure. The picture you chose is one clue I hope you find helpful. What you have been writing in your journal can also include some insights. The more you start directly fulfilling your emotional needs, whatever they are, the more your desire for food will lessen.

• • •

The point is to try and discover what your needs are, and to try and find ways to meet them without using food.

• • •

The purpose of this chart is to push you in a gentle way to be accountable for taking care of yourself. As you understand that urges to overeat come from feelings and the needs they trigger – not food – you need to take action. If our emotional needs continue to be ignored and unsatisfied, we will always "feel" hungry. Taking care of ourselves helps us finally feel "full."

Begin filling in your squares. Please note that in Anne's chart on page 136, she has included plenty of time for her daughter, household chores, and errands. The key word here is balance. We need equal time as our family members, not necessarily more or less, but equal. Anne was able to include other things that allowed her to address her needs. She used the chart as a tool to assist her in taking care of herself. This is a tool you should use, too.

One word of caution: try not to be too rigid with your time. For example, you know that Sundays are always a particularly difficult eating day. In the past when you have had too much unstructured time, you have found yourself in the pantry. Plan a day of shopping, renting a movie, and taking a nap. That's fine. If you suddenly get an opportunity to see a live theater production, please do not say, "I need to stick to my allotted activity and nap!" The chart is there as a preventative medicine and a helper and a guide. It ensures that you'll take care of your emotional self. If you know that you tend to go for food every evening at 10, take a good look at what you really need at that hour. Is it comfort? Then hug your teddy bear. Is it human contact? If married, grab your mate, if not, call a friend. Is it to ventilate frustration? Get out your bat, and swing away. The thing you do not need is food. Eating will feel easier and more comfortable, but only in the short run. In the long run, life's issues remain.

Another reminder: please include your meals in this chart. Eating is a pleasurable part of our day. Never miss a meal or a snack. If your meals are planned and enjoyable, and the day includes meeting emotional needs, you can be pretty certain that a feeling is brewing if suddenly you do have an urge to binge.

Also, include time for grooming. Take that extra five minutes to put some lipstick on or wash your hair. Wear the clothes in your closet that feel good on you.

If you are feeling a bit resistant to the idea of filling out a chart, I can understand that. It takes some time and effort and may be scary. Taking care of your emotional needs for the first time can feel a bit uncomfortable. For example, if your picture, your journal, and your inner voice all suggest that you need more intimacy in your life, and your mate is unwilling or unable to meet these needs, other uncomfortable options may pop into your mind. Divorce, an affair, or even marriage counseling are not alternatives that feel safe. Food is certainly easier and safer. Whatever you discover about yourself and your emotional needs, has probably been "eating away" at you for years. Isn't it time to get everything out in the open and start dealing with yourself and others, instead of the latest diet? Ignoring problems is what has been causing your weight issues. Whether we eat or not, life's issues remain.

Whatever your excuses may be, I encourage you to use the PUF chart. Fill in your week with things that make you FEEL good. Continue to keep your journal, and see how much better you are at diagnosing what you're feeling and figuring out what you need. Remember that your needs are important because you are important. Giving yourself permission to take care of yourself is crucial, so do it!

SAMPLE P.U.F. CHART

	Mon	Tue	Wed	Thu	Fri	Sat	Sun
7-8 AM	← Get up and Dress Me & Beth →						
8-9 AM	← Have Breakfast and Read Paper →						
9-10 AM	Exer.Class	Groc.Shop	Exer.Class	Play Group	Exer.Class	Fmly Outing	Church
10-11 AM	Beth-nursery	Bank/laundry	Beth-nursery		Beth-nursery	Park/zoo/apple	↓
11-12 PM	↓	↓	↓		↓	Pick Movies	Visit Parents
12 PM-1 PM	← Lunch →					Errands/lndry	
1-2 PM	← Beth Naps/Watch Soaps/Clean →					↓	Art Institute
2-3 PM	Read/Sew	Study	Out	Read/Knit	Study	Beth Naps	
3-4 PM	Beth/Park		Beth/lbry	Mall		John & I	↓
4-5 PM	Rent Tape			Sesame St.			
5-6 PM	← Start Dinner/Beth Plays →						Pick Beth Up
6-7 PM	← Eat Dinner →					Get Sitter	Order In
7-8 PM	Clean Up	John Bathes Beth/Reads Story/In Bed				Go Out	
8-9 PM	Watch TV	school	Watch TV	→	Rent Movie		Relax/TV
9-10 PM	Relax/Phone	↓				↓	
10-11 PM	← Time with John →						
11-12 PM	← Sleep →						
12 PM-1 AM	← Sleep (Continued) →						

136

P.U.F. CHART

	Mon	Tue	Wed	Thu	Fri	Sat	Sun
7-8 AM							
8-9 AM							
9-10 AM							
10-11 AM							
11-12 PM							
12 PM-1 PM							
1-2 PM							
2-3 PM							
3-4 PM							
4-5 PM							
5-6 PM							
6-7 PM							
7-8 PM							
8-9 PM							
9-10 PM							
10-11 PM							
11-12 PM							
12 PM-1 AM							

Chapter Nine

Body Image: How Do You Feel About Yours?

I *have discussed feelings,* the emotional needs they trigger, how to fulfill them, and how all are interrelated to emotional overeating. I hope the theme is clear: how we deal with our feelings effects how we eat and how we feel about ourselves. In addition, I hope it's also clear that all of us deserve to have our feelings honored both by others as well as ourselves. We deserve to be treated well. For many people, this issue of "deserving" good things and feelings is a difficult concept to believe. Added to this burden of proof to believe that we are worthwhile enters issues surrounding body image. Our relationship with our body, whatever the present number on the scale reads, just as our relationship with self and others, needs to be examined if permanent change is to occur.

I have often heard desperation in the voices of my clients sharing their dream to be thin. Their hopes and desire is when this magical number on the scale appears, or when they can finally buy the "right" size clothing, they will find happiness. Unfortunately, as many of you may have already experienced, one may reach that magical number only to find that not much in their life has really shifted.

Yes, they may feel better about themselves, but little else has changed. They still have the same marital issues, career decisions, children to contend with, or whatever. It's also common that even with the desired weight loss, they still "feel" fat. The most common occurrence of all is rapid weight gain, often gaining more than they lost. They hate themselves and they hate their bodies, or is it visa versa? Each of us has some powerful preconceived notions about our bodies. We have strong beliefs about how we should look. We have ideas and values about what clothes to wear. These notions, if contributing to low self-esteem, need to be challenged and altered. How did our bodies, their size, and appearance, rather than our inner self begin carrying so much weight? Let's take a look.

SOCIETY

Throughout history, body image and appearance has carried special messages, especially for women. It is beyond the scope of this book to do a complete historic perspective on women and body image. For those interested in a more thorough discussion, Appendix #2 offers several excellent resources. If we were to go back a few centuries and examine the painting of Rubens, we would see that he painted very fleshy, robust women. Being full figured was desirable, and a sign of affluence. At the height of my eating and weight issues, I prayed these norms would return. Thin, wiry women were seen as unattractive and undesirable. In the 1920s the flappers arrived. Flat chests, short hair, and showing leg was the cat's meow. Breasts and curves were hidden. In the 1950s, Marilyn Monroe's curvy, voluptuous figure was ideal. Playboy magazine was showing everything. Miss America was the pageant to watch. Women, their bodies, and sexuality were in the limelight.

Fashion magazines were showing the new woman as beautiful, sexy, and a fabulous homemaker. Even on television, all the TV moms always looked perfect. I never saw Harriet Nelson or June Cleaver with a hair out of place. And in the Reed household, not only did Donna look great, but so did her daughter, Mary. Mary was the ideal teenager with tons of boyfriends, wonderful clothes, and she even had a hit song.

The messages began ringing loud and clear: look good, dress well, have your hair done, cook wonderful meals, and have well behaved children, and your life will be good. But part of the problem was, and is, this concept of "looking good" keeps changing.

In the 1960s, Twiggy came along as the hot new model that women should emulate. No more endowed bosoms like Marilyn's; rather, skin and bones were epitomized. President Kennedy and his beautiful new wife were in the White House. Everybody wanted to know what Jackie was wearing. President Kennedy began discussing physical fitness as an important new part of American life. I'm sure he had no idea that the fitness boom would turn into an American obsession, rather than just a healthy addition to American life.

Peyton Place arrived on our television screens. More beauty and sex! The messages continued that women had to be beautiful and sexy, and their bodies were the key to happiness. Other qualities such as intellect, kindness, warmth, humor, and love were not valued as highly as appearance.

Women felt that they had to act. Their focus was to get their bodies in shape. It was in the 1960s that Jack Lulane began his television workout programs. It was also in the 1960s that Weight Watchers and Overeaters Anonymous began their first group meetings for weight loss. Health clubs began sprouting up everywhere. Weight and body image became a priority for America and especially women.

Another influence also occurred in the 1960s and gathered momentum in the 1970s. This was the Equal Rights Movement. Betty Freidan wrote *The Feminine Mystique* which discussed women's roles. This should have helped women see that they were more than just their bodies. Although the women's rights movement did open doors for new thoughts and ideas, it also created confusion among many women.

Everything in front of them was changing. Their identity was undefined. The new television program that everyone was watching was *Charlie's Angels*. This was about three gorgeous, sexy women who were also tough detectives. Kate Jackson, Farrah Fawcett and Jaclyn Smith were in every fashion magazine. These were the nearly impossible standards women were pressured to achieve. Boy, did they try. Having a perfect body and being sexy were seen as key goals.

The women's movement brought questions out many had

considered but some had not voiced. Should they be home, or should they be working? Should they be sexy, or should they burn their bras and wear no make up? How could we be both sexy and assertive? How and who were the women to follow? The one thing women believed that they could control was their weight. The other questions about children, career, and marriage, may not have felt so easy to address. However, their weight and their body, so they thought, were within the realms of easy change. As the diet programs multiplied and graced every book shelf with promises of a better marriage, more success and inner peace, the more women signed on the dotted line.

By the 1980s, concern for appearance was transformed into an American obsession. The baby boomers were of age and became the consumers' consumer. Looks, money, and affluence was everything. Jane Fonda began selling her workouts, and "feeling the burn" became an aspired goal. On television, *Dynasty* was a show we all turned on to watch. This program gave glamour and glitz a whole new definition. Billy Crystal's quote, "Dahling, you look mahvelous," was on everyone's lips. If you look good, then you'll feel good. If only that were true. It was also in the 1980s that Karen Carpenter died of anorexia.

It is now the 1990s. Hopefully this is the decade in which we will reexamine some of our past ideals. Cindy Crawford is a popular model. Her body is a bit fuller than those of hit models in the past; still, how many of us will ever really look like Cindy Crawford? But perhaps more important is the reason we place that as such a desirable and meaningful goal. I want you to begin examining your values and ideas about your body and appearance. The popular saying, "You can never be too rich or too thin," says all too clearly where America's values lie. Beauty and appearance are seen as all-important. This is the problem.

Certainly, there is nothing wrong with caring about your body and appearance. Exercise too, as I will discuss later, can be a wonderfully healthy part of life. The key phrase here is "part of life." When grooming and exercise are done joyfully and as a part of self-care, this is wonderful. However, when your entire self worth is based on the number on the scale, or the size of your latest purchase, there is something askew.

• • •

Begin examining your values and ideas about your body and appearance.

• • •

We are all so much more than our body size. Accepting and learning to love ourselves means to love our body no matter what its shape or size. Our society has taken a path in an unhealthy direction. We do not have to follow this path.

FAMILY

History and society have had a big impact on how women feel about their bodies. What we learned in our family is equally influential. I find myself thinking about Irene. An attractive single woman, she came to my office at age 31. Her outfits were carefully coordinated with lovely accessories. Her long curly hair, make up, and nails were beautifully groomed. It was clear that she cared a lot about her appearance. Irene was successful as a professional in computer sales.

She had several close friends; in fact many of her co-workers admired her. She freely could describe herself as a nice and caring person. None of the preceding qualities made up for the fact that she was fifty pounds overweight.

When Irene looked in the mirror, she only saw a fat person. Her beautiful hair, her knack for putting nice outfits together, her wonderful friendships, and her caring nature were never acknowledged. If complemented on her appearance or on a nice gesture, her response would be negative. She would often scrunch up her face in disgust, making some kind of comment suggesting that the person needed glasses, or that the deed was "no big deal." She could not feel or see anything good about her inner self, or her body. This attitude about herself would change only after she lost weight.

We began to explore her family origin. Irene was the oldest of three children. She has two younger brothers. Her father worked in retail, and her mom stayed home, for the most part, to raise the kids. Her maternal grandmother, a native European, lived with the family. She and her husband came to this country for greater opportunities. Although they raised a family and made a decent living, she never really achieved what she hoped to. Granny, as Irene called her, was a very bitter and angry woman. During her adult life, she was consumed with appearance. Since she did not achieve the financial success for which she hoped, she compensated by always looking her best. This included watching her diet. Granny spent a tremendous amount of time criticizing and judging everyone else's appearance. Granny was always thin, but Irene's mom and Irene had to watch what they ate. Genetically, their bodies were different, (more about genetics later) however, Granny couldn't stand it that they did not look perfect.

Granny would lock the cabinets to try and "help" her daughter and granddaughter with their weight problem. She did most of the cooking and would portion out their meals. Whenever they went to a restaurant, Granny would comment on what the family ingested, and what everyone else in the restaurant would eat. Included in these comments would be a critique of the attire of everyone that passed their table. All Granny cared about was the image that was presented. Your character, and acts of kindness were never acknowledged, let alone valued.

Irene was continually criticized for her eating habits and body weight while she was growing up. There wasn't a day that went by that Granny did not remind Irene how to stand, to wear a girdle, to eat right, and to carefully coif her hair.

If for any reason Irene did not adhere to Granny's suggestions, the emotional abuse began. Criticism after nasty criticism was bestowed on Irene. What made all this even more painful was the fact that Irene's mother did not come to her defense. Not only was her body weight continually attacked, but there was no one there to defend her. Irene learned at a very young age that her body and appearance were not okay, and without anyone's support, she felt alone and uncared about.

Messages from families can be powerful. Each of us have learned a variety of values from our families. These values include how we feel about our bodies. Irene, as with many other people, learned that looks and appearance were highly valued commodities. She then integrated these beliefs into her self-image.

Through therapy, she began to understand why she was so critical of herself and her overall appearance. With this new insight to her unhealthy family dynamics, she could then begin to move forward, implementing new, healthier ideas and values about her body and her inner self.

It is important for you to look back to see how your family regarded looks and body image. If your family was open about body functions, touching, sexuality, and relaxed with meals, rarely discussing appearance or weight, chances are you're comfortable with your body image. But if you came from a family where touching was uncomfortable, and food, weight and looks were a big topic of conversation, it's likely that unpleasant issues surrounding your body image need to be explored.

Wherever your family is on the spectrum of looks and body comfort, you can create your own new relationship with your body, no matter what your weight. The fantasy that you will like your body when it's at that magical number is just that – a fantasy.

The way to feel better about your body is to begin today.

I Always Start . . . .

I recommend that you begin by conversing with your body in a loving manner. Begin by picking the part of your body that you like the most, or hate the most. Tell this part of your body that you love it, and are going to be kind to it. If it's a part you can stroke, go ahead. This should all be done in a very loving, kind manner. Take this slowly.

As you begin this exercise, you may feel a bit foolish, or not believe what you are telling yourself. That's okay, just do it. There are also several wonderful books that I have included in the bibliography that are very helpful in teaching women how to love their bodies.

Our inner souls are housed in our bodies. We need to cherish this house just as we cherish the home we live in. And if our home has one messy room, would we criticize the entire house? So it should be with our bodies. There may very well be one part of your anatomy that does not please you, but this does not mean that the entire you deserves to be put down and unappreciated. And if you are thinking, there is not a part of my outer body that I'm pleased with, you must come back to your inner self, for here is where the true you resides.

GENETICS

In a chapter on body image it's also important to address genetics. Like it or not, we are all born with certain predetermined genes. Some of us are tall, some are short. Some of us have dark hair, and some of us have light. Some are wonderful athletes, and some are talented musicians. Some of us are thin, and some of us are heavy. These are the facts, and it's time to consider these truisms when exploring weight issues.

If you were to pick up a high school biology book, there would, inevitably, be a section discussing the three most common body types.

These types are labeled:

ECTOMORPH= Thin body frame
ENDOMORPH= Fleshy body frame
MESOMORPH= Muscular body frame

According to research, we are each genetically predispositioned to one of these particular body types. If this is true, which I believe it is, we need to respect our body type. This is not to say that if you are one hundred pounds overweight and your health is in jeopardy, you should give up trying to take off some weight. What it does suggest, however, is that you see from your bone structure and your family history that you're an endomorph body type. Quit driving yourself crazy to achieve Twiggy's silhouette.

● ● ●
We need to respect our body type.
● ● ●

On the same avenue is the setpoint theory. This theory, similar to the predetermined body type approach, suggests that for each of us there is an inborn ideal body weight. This weight is unique for each of us. This setpoint is not really an exact number; rather, it's a range of several pounds.

The body is literally programmed to help us stay within this unique range. Since our bodies work to keep us healthy and alive, if we start messing with this range, our bodies will do what they must to survive.

If we are on the same crazy diet that is pushing our bodies below this setpoint, our body's metabolism may slow down or we may find that we are hungrier. Be assured, something will occur to help us reach our healthy weight. Nature incorporated this self-protection to allow us to survive periods of famine.

I Always Start . . . .

Nature did not expect so many of us to purposely starve ourselves.

When you try to push yourself to go below this setpoint range, you will, and may already have, experience a great deal of frustration. As I mentioned in chapter one, I read that Jaclyn Smith was 5'8" tall, and weighed 115 pounds. Since I was 5'7, I thought that I, too, should weigh 115 pounds. I may have achieved that weight for one minute! However, I soon realized that this was an unrealistic goal for myself and my body. For me to maintain that weight, I would have had to eat carrot sticks and lettuce for the rest of my life, plus exercise three hours a day.

I had to come to terms with who I was, what I liked to eat, how I felt about exercise, and what was realistic for my body and lifestyle. I also had to be willing to change my ideal weight and accept that I would not be as thin as Jaclyn. After awhile, thank goodness, I was so frustrated with my inability to achieve this standard, I gave it up. I was willing to examine myself and change my relationship with food, the scale, and myself. If this meant being a bit heavier, but being able to eat normally and not be so concerned with my body, this was okay by me. You, too, need to come to terms with a realistic weight for your body, genetically and emotionally.

How do you know what your setpoint range is? It's usually helpful to take a written weight history of yourself and your family. Jot down your weight range over the last several years. Take into consideration your activity level. If you have done a great deal of "yo-yo" dieting, your setpoint may be a little higher (again, our bodies are our protectors). Keep in mind your age and hormonal factors.

Then see if you can come up with a reasonable range. It may be a ten pound range or a twenty pound range. Then try and eat normally for two months. If you are journaling, fulfilling your emotional needs, and doing your PUF chart, your ability to eat well should be greater. The main thing to remember is that not everyone is supposed to weigh the same.

This is a hard concept to let go of if you have been dieting your entire life. It would be boring if we all looked the same. Isn't variety the spice of life? All of this is really about accepting and liking yourself for who you are – deemphasize your shape and emphasize your soul.

EXERCISE

Unless you've not watched the news or read a newspaper, you are aware of how beneficial regular and appropriate exercise can be to your age and stamina. I would not call the kind of exercise that most chronic dieters pursue regular or appropriate. Often, they partake in heavy duty aerobics, several times a day. Or they only exercise when they start their latest diet. I suggest exercising in moderation, respecting your body and your lifestyle.

If you would like to lose weight, increasing your exercise will help. I'm sure that you are aware of that. What is really important to consider is choosing an exercise program that fits you, not what everyone else is doing. Do what you feel you will enjoy, and stick with it.

This entails being honest with how you feel about physical activity. Some people really love it; others think it's tolerable, and others, still, hate it. Wherever you fit on this continuum needs to be honored before you begin to create a liveable exercise program.

If you're a beginner, I recommend that you check with your physician before starting any new exercise regime. Assuming that you're healthy, I usually recommend beginning with walking. It takes the least amount of effort and money. Begin with a 10 minute walk and work your way up to 30-40 minutes. Try to enjoy your activity. Listen to some music or find a friend to join you. Some people enjoy the time alone to think. Try to do the walking (or whatever you choose) at least three times a week. Just remember the three C's of any new exercise program:

Use your COMMON SENSE. If any activity hurts or does not feel right, discontinue it. "Feeling the burn" is not my philosophy!

Be CONSISTENT. The real benefits of any activity are usually felt after about four weeks of regular (3 times a week) activity.

Be CONSERVATIVE. A slower start will result in fewer injuries, and greater feelings of accomplishment. Your body will tell you when to increase the intensity and duration of your activity. If you listen to your body, you should progress naturally and easily.

As with everything I have discussed, if exercise will help you feel better about yourself and be more comfortable with your body, incorporate it into your life. If it's used as a punishment for your weight, it will not work. If each time you exercise you are running to the scale to see how much you have lost, you are not using exercise in a helping manner.

I hope my approach to exercise is clear. I think that when used in an appropriate manner, it can be a wonderful benefit to everyone's longevity of life. When it's used obsessively and compulsively and only as a means for weight loss, I think more harm than good is done.

THE SCALE

Many of my clients have a closer relationship with their scale than they do with anyone else! How can such a small piece of machinery have so much impact on self-esteem? This, too, needs to change. I have had clients weighing themselves as often as five times a day, others as frequently as twice daily, and still others only in the morning, while nude after going to the bathroom! Whatever the number portrayed determined their mood. If the number was lower than the previous weigh-in, then they felt good. This became a problem. If they felt thin, they gave themselves permission to eat a little more that day. Afterwards, they felt "fat" and bad again. If the number on the scale was higher than they hoped, this, too, was bad. They were so frustrated that they turned to food. Weighing was always a no-win experience.

I recommend weighing yourself as little as possible. I have encouraged many of my clients to get rid of their scale. What is the difference what the scale reads? If you are eating normally and in a healthy manner, you know it, and in time, your body will show it.

If you have overeaten, you're quite aware of your behavior. You do not need a scale to remind you and make you feel worse. If you're shaking at the thought of not weighing yourself, then do so at the doctor's office, preferably twice a month.

Make sure that you have someone you can trust to process how you feel about the number that appeared. Frequently people reach a plateau after eating well for a while. This may cause anger or frustration, and people decide that a large snack would feel pretty good. For this reason, it's important to have someone with you to support your feelings. Always remember that you are much more than your body or what the scale reads!

As women, much of our self-esteem has been judged by our appearance. Women's automatic thought processes often center around looks. They feel that if a man does not want to be with them, it's due to their weight. If a job promotion fell through, it's a result of their size. Even worse are the women who do not put themselves out there for the relationship or the job because they feel they're only as good as they are close to their ideal size. This needs to stop. Women need to see that they're much more than a body or a number on a scale. It's time to stop hiding who we are. One's self image should not be based on the size of one's thighs.

Chapter Ten
The Mourning Process: Letting Go

In the last nine chapters I have encouraged you to look deep inside yourself. I have asked you to examine your relationship with food and begin replacing old thoughts and rules with healthier ideas. I have asked you to look at your emotions and how they relate to your eating. I have offered new ways to deal with these emotions. I have pushed you to re-examine your relationship with your body and challenge society's norms. And I have asked you to try and stay in touch with and listen to your own very special and unique inner voice. Now I want you to take it a step further.

As already stated in the beginning of this book, change is a process. It's not something that is done in one day and it's over. Change is a continuous process of learning and letting go of the old. This letting go of the old is what the following pages discuss. Before you read on, please keep in mind the process I am about to introduce is just that – a process. So take your time. Do it in stages. Do it whatever ways feel best for you. As with everything else I have discussed, doing this mourning process is an individual decision and needs to be executed in a manner fitting your particular personality and level of readiness. As always, respect and honor your inner self.

By this time it should be pretty evident that your emotional reactions to food are due to unresolved feelings as well as unmet needs. It should also be clear to break this unhealthy repetitious cycle, it's essential to address these feelings and needs directly, whether via hugging, journaling, meditating, taking a class or reframing the situation. Eating never resolves life issues. Ingesting food just makes life feel better for the moment.

However, giving up something you have used as a source of comfort is difficult. It's almost like losing a dear friend.

I Always Start . . . .

Upon losing someone close, most of us need to go through a mourning period. That's exactly what you need to do: say good bye to the part of you that has used food as a way of coping.

• • •
Always respect and honor your inner self.
• • •

When I have helped clients begin the mourning process, many are ready and eager to let go of the old, uncomfortable part of self. They cannot imagine this could be a difficult experience to undertake. So many have hated the part of self that ate uncontrollably, and they can't wait to let "her" go. But there is often resistance in the actual process. This part of you may not be a part that you love or are proud of, but it is and has been for years a key ingredient to your survival. To let it go and say good bye brings on many mixed feelings. Just as leaving a job that wasn't totally satisfying or moving from a home that you have outgrown brings on both relief and sadness, so does saying good bye to the part of you that has inappropriately used food. But just as starting a new job or moving to a new home helps relieve sad feelings, building a new, healthier you helps dissipate the uncomfortable feelings of saying good bye to the old you.

The mourning process is very important in the permanent process of change. It will allow you to get in touch with the pain your eating has caused – and let go of it. The mourning process frees you. Here is how you begin.

I would like you to find a very large cardboard box or huge plastic garbage bag. You are going to fill it with some very significant items that symbolize the part of you that has used food to deal with emotions. This is the part of you that

you want to permanently part from. Below are the items that
go into your mourning box or bag.

ANYTHING IN YOUR CLOSET THAT'S
- TOO SMALL
- TOO UGLY
- REMINDING YOU OF YOUR OVEREATING SELF

I want you to go through your wardrobe and pull out any
clothing that makes you feel fat, unattractive, or that was
favorite "eating" attire. Those loose sweat pants, that old,
stained robe, that oversized T-shirt or whatever you own that
you do not feel good wearing. You are to rid your closet of
any reminders of the you that turned to unhealthy eating as a
way to cope. This also includes clothes that are a size six from
that one day you could wear such an unrealistic size.
Remember: the you that went on crazy diets is being replaced
with a new, improved, healthier you. These old clothes are
representative of a part of you that's no longer needed. Give
these clothes to the needy. As you continue to feel better
about yourself, you'll allow yourself to purchase some new
items. Taking care of your appearance is still going to be a
part of self care, so I want you to have clothes that you not
only feel comfortable in but also attractive. Being well
groomed on the outside is often a reflection of how one feels
on the inside.

ALL YOUR OLD DIET BOOKS — EXCEPT THIS ONE

This is another important component of the mourning
process. You no longer need detailed plans of what to eat or
how many calories are ingested each day. If you do need a
guideline, you can always refer to Appendix 1. Most diet
books are filled with gimmicks and fads that are not only
unhealthy, but encourage you to stay enmeshed in the entire
mentality of dieting. I want you to leave this community.
Seeking quick remedies to a weight problem is reminiscent of

I Always Start . . . .

the old you. The new you will be turning to books discussing your entire well being, or novels, or whatever pleases you.

A LIST OF ALL OLD EXCUSES AND SAYINGS

On a piece of paper, jot down common thought patterns that might include "I'll start my diet on Monday," or "I've already blown my diet, so I might as well eat everything in sight," or "It's New Year's Eve." This list can go on and on. You probably have several of your own rationalizations you have used when turning to food. These rationales apply to the symptoms, but don't address the underlying issues. In the bag they go.

OLD PICTURES

Go through your old photographs and remove any that remind you of a time when you were not feeling good about yourself due to your weight and/or your eating habits on a particular day. This could be a picture taken at a party; though you're smiling, you remember how awful you felt about yourself. I want you to pull out photos reminding you of the you that suppressed your feelings and needs and ate instead – the part of you that you want to leave behind.

LABELS/WRITTEN NAMES OF FAVORITE BINGE FOODS

This is a very important part of your mourning bag. I want you to be in touch with the foods you've abused in the past. If you have any of these foods in the house, you may cut the labels off and put them in your bag. If not, jot down the names of your favorite pig out foods on index cards, one item per card. For example, if you always turned to potato chips under emotional turmoil, the words POTATO CHIPS should be written on the index card. If your favorite binge food was doughnuts, then that word should be written on a different card. I want you to be thinking of foods that you felt controlled you in the past – rather than the other way around. These labels and index cards are going to help you in feeling your past behaviors and make it easier to let go.

OTHER REMINDERS

If you can think of anything else reminding you of the person who used food to cope with life, in the bag it goes. Miscellaneous things that come to mind might include gifts you have kept because you were being so-o-o-o nice instead of returning it for something you desired; or an invitation to a party you accepted out of obligation, attended and ate rather than excusing yourself at the onset or at least exiting early. Anything representing you not being kind to yourself should be part of this process.

Putting this bag together should take some time, so don't hurry. The contents should make an impact on you. After you've gathered your items and placed them in your bag, set the bag aside for a few days. Give yourself time to reflect. Pulling together all the contents assuredly brought on a variety of feelings. Take some time to journal about these emotions before returning to your bag. After a few days have passed and you have given yourself some time to reflect, you will be ready to begin the actual mourning process – saying good bye to that part of you that did not validate and honor your true inner self.

When you feel you're ready, here's how you begin. Each day, put aside five or ten minutes to go through your bag. You should be in a quiet, private place with some soft music playing , or in total silence if your prefer. Wherever you are, you should feel safe from interruption. Open your bag and begin going through its contents. Examine the collection piece by piece. Sometimes it's helpful to have your teddy bear handy or your whiffle bat. Getting in touch with this old part of you usually brings on both sadness and anger – sadness at the time wasted overeating, dieting and obsessing about appearance and anger for the same reasons. As you go through the items, feel them, remembering how you felt when you wore the clothes or ate the food. If while doing this you are not feeling deep sadness and anger, your bag is not filled with the best items. It is important to feel the loss.

You may be feeling, "Why do I need to feel pain in order to move on?" Sometimes while living life less than to its fullest, we find ways to cover up our discomfort. We push our uncomfortable feelings away. As long as these feelings stay emersed, we cannot grow. Going through the mourning process is extremely helpful in pushing people to be honest with the pain their old ways insured. The more in touch you are with your previously suppressed uncomfortable feelings, the less likely you are to want to return to the lifestyle that allowed that pain to exist. As these old painful feelings surface, and one's desire to repeat experiencing these feelings decline, the more we are apt to approach the deep waters of change with less angst. Going through your bag should help you feel a sense of sadness and emptiness, as well as anger for time lost – time now you can look at as time needed to get you where you are today and future destinations. The stronger your feelings of loss, the more the odds are in your favor you'll avoid returning to unhealthy coping mechanisms.

Spend at least a week going through this process. If you need more time, fine. Saying good bye to a part of you is not easy. As you go through your bag you'll probably be in touch with your imperfections, things most of us try to hide. But being able to accept our imperfections is part of life. Through self acceptance comes inner peace. When we feel peaceful, we don't overeat. As you go through your bag, it's perfectly okay to cry, scream, pout, or do whatever you need to do in order to feel the sense of loss and the readiness to say good bye.

● ● ●

Being able to accept our imperfections is part of life. Through self acceptance comes inner peace.

● ● ●

When you feel you've gotten in touch with the sadness and anger at having been enmeshed with food and weight issues, you're ready to discard your bag. Find a large dumpster and bring your bag to it. The more symbolic, the better. Wear something fresh and new to the "burial." We want to symbolize the burying of the parts of you that often made you feel like you were dying – those parts that ignored your needs, whether emotional, spiritual, intellectual, sexual or physical. Dumping this bag is a symbolic way of ending your old way of living life – a way that was hurtful. Sometimes this farewell needs to be said more than once. That's okay. It's a process. When you're ready, place the bag inside the dumpster. Say some words if you wish. Stand and think awhile, and when you feel you're done, walk away.

Be prepared. You may experience some sadness for the next few days or even longer. Again, this is understandable. The "eating" has been with you a long time. If you need some winding down time, then whatever that means to you, do it. If that means taking a day off work, then give yourself a mental health day. If that means sending the kids off to friends, then that's fine, too. The new you respects her feelings and needs.

After you begin feeling a bit better, it's time to create a new symbol for the new you. You need to find another bag or box. I want this container to be beautiful. In it goes the following:

PHOTOGRAPHS – These should be beautiful pictures that

make you feel good. They could be of a wonderful place you have been to or would like to see. It could be a photo of a family gathering where you felt joy. The photos should all represent a peaceful, loving feeling, the kind you want to regularly experience.

NEW SAYINGS – Jot down inspirational thoughts you can refer to when having a difficult time. The new you knows life has its various ups and downs but needs new ways of dealing with these hills and valleys. Some helpful thoughts might include,"I am entitled to my feelings"; or "I am not a bad person because I'm angry"; or "I have many wonderful qualities and they are..." Staying in touch with your inside is essential for inner peace.

NEW GOALS – Make a list of some activities you'd love to try but have avoided because of your weight. I have one client who's going sky diving, but your goals don't have to be that extreme. They may include going to the beach with your friends and family or taking a class. Putting these thoughts in writing can increase the odds of you achieving what you want and deserve.

REASSESS YOUR VALUES AND PRIORITIES — Many people live their lives using values they learned as children. Though some of these may by satisfactory to hold on to, some usually need revamping. Take time out to think about what is important to you and in what order. If family is an important value but you dread spending time with Mom and Dad, explore what kind of changes need to transpire. Look at your work. How much time are you spending there? What about your leisure time? Where does that fit into your life? Reassessing and prioritizing validates your feelings and needs. Jot your ideas down and put them in the bag.

● ● ●

The new you respects her feelings and needs.

● ● ●

Unlike the mourning bag, the "new you" bag does not get thrown away. It gets kept forever and is continually growing. I suggest you go through your "new you" bag every day for about five or ten minutes. You can turn on some lively music. As you go through the bag, feel how different you are and continue to become. As you look at your photos, read your sayings, evaluate your goals and reassess your values, check in with your inner gut and see how you feel. You should notice a more joyful feeling. The "new you" will now be an ongoing, learning and growing phenomenon. This bag will symbolize your growth. The more the "new you" is solidified through respecting your feelings and needs, treating yourself with the same love and kindness you have given others, eating the foods you love in appropriate proportions, and staying in tune with your inner self, the more your weight issues will stay in the dumpster.

Chapter Eleven
I Always Start My Life Today

In *the previous chapter* as well as throughout this book, I've discussed being in touch with your inner gut feelings. I have encouraged you to look at yourself, your feelings, and your life and use your gut as your guide. In the first chapter I mentioned not having the definitive answer to why and how this gut guiding system works, just that it does. Though I still feel I may not know the absolute answers, I've done enough reading and personal soul searching to feel comfortable sharing the ideas I've found helpful in dealing with my own life.

What I'm about to present may feel foreign to you and if it does, that's understandable. A hundred years ago the idea that man could one day walk on the moon was not only foreign but seen as ridiculous. Looking deeper into our spirituality, our purposes, may also feel unfamiliar initially and even ridiculous. Yet it is in each of our souls where true joy lives. Our entire planet is moving into a direction of higher consciousness. I believe, as one hundred years ago space travel seemed unheard of and is now a matter of course, so too will it become routine for humans to be in touch with their own unique souls. With all of that shared, I want to encourage you to read the entire chapter. While reading, be with your inner gut and see how you feel. This chapter will not do justice to all the material available on soul exploration, but I want to give you a flavor of the concepts. If you find it interesting, turn to the list of suggested readings where I've listed some wonderful resources to help you in your own search for life's true meaning.

You might wonder why – in a book about conquering your food and weight issues – a chapter on soul searching and the meaning of life would be important. The answer to this question is weighted (excuse the pun) on a belief system that

I Always Start . . . .

I believe to be true. After 20 years of introspection, I hope what I've learned helps.

From a very young age, I questioned the meaning and purpose of life. Even as a young girl I'd wonder about my body, and what it was made of and how it functioned so well without me doing a thing. Was my body who I was or was it my inner self? What made these thoughts come into my head? They were pretty heady questions for a young person to be asking. Since I thought they were weird, too, I never explored them with anyone. I kept these thoughts and feelings hidden.

As I moved into my teenage years many of these concerns subsided. I was more interested in my boyfriend and social activities. This disconcern for my inner self continued right through college, marriage and pregnancy. It was after my son was born that suddenly the questions returned. Who was this new life? How would I raise him? What would I do with the rest of my life? Was I really happy in this marriage – all very scary questions. As previously mentioned, this was the time my eating disorder manifested.

After years of bingeing, dieting and excessive exercising, I sought help and began exploring the deeper questions in my life. My exploration not only included psychological issues but much broader life issues. "What is the meaning of Life?" kept recurring. I also questioned why I had to suffer so with my eating disorder, why I was unhappy in my marriage, and why other people seemed to have such easy lives. Why? Why? Why?

I always believed there was some great power that created the universe. When I saw the trees changing with the seasons or the appearance of the moon or the births of my children – all so well-planned and organized – there had to be some power who created this magic. For the ease of writing and common terminology, I've chosen to call this super power God. If using that name makes you uncomfortable, but you believe there is some larger creator, feel free to replace God with whatever term you wish. The concept of God was not something I needed to be convinced about. But the question of why he created the human race kept surfacing. What was our purpose as a race and more specifically, what was my individual purpose?

As you read what follows, I encourage you to keep an open mind and an open gut. It is a summary of my thoughts on why we're here on Earth and what my purpose seems to be. It's up to you to explore what your purpose is.

It's my feeling that God is the creator of the universe. He is all-knowing and all-loving. He became lonely, so decided he needed friends. He began creating souls – entities filled with love to keep him company and help him create. A glitch occurred. He created many, many souls who began taking on lives of their own and doing things that troubled God. The souls even agreed they weren't being God-like, but couldn't seem to learn from their mistakes. So God decided these souls he so loved needed to learn lessons that would help them grow, learn and love unconditionally.

God had already created Earth with all its wonders. On Earth there would be physical limitations that were not issues in the heavens. God pondered the dilemma for awhile and decided to create human beings. Into each of these beings he would put a soul. The soul would agree to use time on Earth to learn, grow, and ultimately, love. The soul would leave the physical body, return to God and discuss what ensued during its Earthly life. If it turned out that the soul learned only a portion of the lessons, it would then opt to return to Earth for continued education. A soul might need to return numerous times. With its lessons completed, it returns to God in its final Earthly incarnation to reside permanently in total love and harmony on this higher plane, ready to assist other souls on their journey.

Everything that happens on Earth – and more specifically in your life – has a reason and purpose, including eating and weight issues. Your soul does not want you to avoid your life lessons. When you do, it finds ways to get your attention, creating some uncomfortable situation that pushes you to look deeper. A soul only wants us to grow, learn and love. Sometimes this means life will be difficult. Whatever difficulty you may be experiencing, it always presents an opportunity for growth. Your soul wants you to spiritually learn. Before coming to Earth, your soul, along with God and your guides (more about guides later) created a plan for this lifetime. When you're not on the right path, your soul will do what it can to get your attention, which can be an eating disorder, drug problem or illness. As far as your soul is concerned, learning is everything.

• • •

Your soul does not want you to avoid your life lessons. When you do, it finds a way to get your attention.

• • •

If what I'm saying is true – that we all have a predestined path – does this mean we really have no control over our lives? No! God's plan was two-fold. First, we do not have a memory of our soul's agreement, so learning is much more challenging. Second, we're given personalities and brains with which to think, question and make decisions. Both parts of The Plan are present to make our learning experience as meaningful and challenging as possible. As with anything in life, when we put more time and energy into a learning process, we remember and learn at a higher level. This is certainly true with the ultimate challenge of soul development.

Remember that the number one goal is not to suffer but to learn. To do this, we may need to experience what appears to be pain and suffering – and to our personalities and bodies it is. This perceived pain is always about learning and growth. When you come to accept this concept, it makes more sense out of our "tragedies." It's because of your eating/weight issues that you are searching for more answers. Without this stressful issue in your life, you may not have pushed yourself to look deeper.

No matter what the problem, it is a tool for your education. My eating disorder, my divorce, and the challenges of living as a single parent for many years were, in retrospect, gifts. Without these difficult issues in my life, I wouldn't be where I am today – personally and professionally. Some people have more painful challenges than others. This is where deeper questions are asked. The larger the pain, the more learning that is needed. Cancer, loss of a loved one, a disability or poverty – awful as these issues are, God and our soul and our guides bring them to us not as punishment, but out of love and recognition of our learning needs.

I have mentioned the term "guides" and each of us have at least one and often, several. Let me explain what a guide does. Before we choose to return to our school on Earth, we get together with God and several guides. Guides are souls that have completed all their Earthly work and achieved a permanent status as God's partner. Each guide is wise beyond anything we can imagine. While on Earth, our guide is there to help us and offer guidance. Before returning to Earth our souls sit and chat with God and the guide(s) thought to be most useful during our upcoming lives. Together, we all decide the purpose of this incarnation. We decide who our parents will be, our siblings, our mates, our children. All we choose to interact with in this life are to help us – and them – grow and learn. Many of these souls are people we knew in past lives and still need to complete some unfinished learning. Our guides are usually connected with the important people in our lives. If we could learn to be in touch with our inner gut feelings, we will also be in touch with our guide(s).

• • •

All we choose to interact with in this life are to help us – and them – grow and learn.

• • •

We "choose" our families. If you come from an abusive home, it would only be natural to wonder why you would choose to be with these souls. The answer is your soul needed to be with these people to learn and they needed to be with you for the same purpose. You may be thinking your parents have not learned a thing and never will. It may seem so. When they physically die they may very well need to reassess and return to Earth for continuing life lessons. Just as we are all different ages here on Earth, so are our souls. Some of us are newer souls. These are people who usually take life very simply. They don't ask deeply spiritual questions. The older the soul, the more the search for higher meaning. This doesn't mean a newer soul is not as good as an older soul – just that it's on a different path.

Wherever you are on your path, being in touch with your guide makes life more manageable. How do you get in touch with your guide? Practice, practice, practice. Like anything else, this takes work. Most believe the best route to connecting with your spiritual guide is via meditation. I've included a few books on meditation in the bibliography, but if you would like to begin now, just sit somewhere comfortable and do some deep breathing. Think of a question that troubles you. Ask your guide for help. Then just wait. Sometime soon, maybe right now or later in the day or perhaps tomorrow, something will hit you and you'll "know" what you need to do.

You might ask, "How do I know the answer came from

my guide or higher self and not just from my brain?" You will know because the answer will feel right. Whenever you have this "feel right" experience, you'll know you're on the right track.

We could use your eating as an example. When you use food inappropriately, it feels wrong. There's a strong part of you that knows this is not the way you want to lead your life. You may get that same "wrong" sense when you have treated someone rudely or were unkind. This is your inner self, your guide, trying to get your attention. It's not that your feelings are right or wrong. As I've repeated, feelings are not right or wrong. They just are. It's how you handle these feelings that determines your self esteem and feelings of peace. If you deal with them directly, healthily, lovingly without abusing food, you feel good – very, very good.

It is this feeling good that I want you to regularly experience. Following the exercises I have offered in the previous pages – plus looking at your soul's calling – will allow you to feel very, very good. It took me many years to achieve this inner peace. I needed to recover from my eating disorder, leave an unfulfilling marriage, and raise two children as a single parent. At the time I wouldn't have looked at these experiences as any kind of gift of higher learning. In retrospect, though, that's just what they were. Due to those very painful periods, I did learn and grow. I found a career I love. I built a wonderful relationship with my children that I believe would never be what it is if I'd stayed unhappily married – and I built a wonderful relationship with myself. Again, during the time of my eating disorder and divorce did I feel happy that I was in this learning period? Hardly! But I can now say I'm grateful for my struggles. Is my present life perfect? Of course not, but now I know life in not meant to be perfect. I am in school. And I don't know about you, but when I was in high school, college and graduate school, I wasn't generally happy all the time. There were classes I enjoyed, teachers I found wonderful. There were other classes that were not as enjoyable, teachers not so wonderful. But through it all, I learned and grew.

So it is with the school of Earthly life. There are times that are enjoyable and wonderful. There are other times that this isn't so. But both parts of life should be seen as important, exciting and challenging, because it's all really about learning and growing to a much higher, deeper, peaceful place. And an essential part of this learning and growing also includes trusting – trusting that God will be there to help you in what you need in life, not necessarily in terms of what your personality desires but in terms of your soul's standards and needs. Your personality is there to act out your soul's purpose. The problem is that your personality often takes on a mind of its own. This is where free will enters the life picture. When your personality is aligned with you inner soul, your life feels alive. As one teacher once shared with me, it's like keeping a valve open. When you're open to your spirituality which is absent of fear and full of love, you feel joy. When the valve is closed, watch out. You are doing life without a life jacket.

• • •

Your answers are inside you. I hope you start each day looking there, inside yourself.

• • •

This is a very difficult premise to understand. But everything I have experienced, read and learned validates that staying attuned to your gut, your guide, your higher self and God makes you feel good. You will have to explore these concepts to see if it's so for you. But your soul brought you to this book rather than to another diet book. Perhaps as you reflect on the experiences of your life, situations and events you might have chalked up to coincidence you might find something more if you examine them further. Painful events can perhaps be seen as important turning points.

I wish you the best of luck in your search. Remember, food is not the answer to your life issues. Starting a new diet on Monday is also not the answer. Your answers are inside you. I hope you start each day looking there, inside yourself. Trust me. Trust your guide. You will not be sorry and you will feel very, very good.

Afterward

The *majority of this book* addresses feelings and how to identify and deal with them in healthy ways. But as I have mentioned, sometimes we may need extra help. If you find you are doing quite a bit of inner work via journaling, talking with friends, meditating, and other ways – and you are still feeling depressed, frustrated, anxious, or just not able to handle life – it would be an appropriate time to seek professional assistance via a therapist. Below is the name of a national referral service. It is free and is happy to recommend licensed therapists in your area. Your physician or a good friend are also viable resources. Once you have a few names, it is perfectly acceptable to set up an interview. This is going to be a significant relationship, so you want to make sure it feels right.

I have found that though degrees and credentials are important, ultimately it's how you feel about the person. Is this someone you can relate to? Did you feel comfortable? Did you feel s/he understood your feelings? If your answers are negative, I don't care how many degrees and credentials grace the wall – move on.

Assuming you have found the right therapist, and you are both working hard, if relief is not forthcoming, please keep medication as an option. The more I have worked in the counseling field, the more I am convinced many syndromes have a genetic and bio-chemical component. Many of these disorders such as depression, anxiety, compulsive/obsessive disorder and bulimia/anorexia respond beautifully to medication in conjunction with psychotherapy. Many are still so cautious about taking anti-depressants and other meds, they needlessly suffer much longer than necessary.

I encourage you to follow your gut instincts – if medication does not feel right, then certainly honor that – but try and at least get all the information from your doctor so you can make an informed decision. No one likes being on medication, but if there is a chemical reason for your depression, just as diabetics need insulin, so it is that you may need an anti-depressant.

Good luck with your lessons. Feel free to contact me. I love receiving feedback!

Free referral source:
ANAD (Anorexia Nervosa & Associated Disorders)
PO Box 7
Highland Park, IL 60035
847.831.3438

My address:
Janice Alpert, M.A., L.C.P.C.
540 Frontage Road #2045
Northfield, IL 60093
847.441.5470
FAX 847.446.8618
Janice 983@aol.com

Healthy Eating
by Marla Heller, R.D., L.D.

Healthy eating is about enjoying food. Eating well is one of life's greatest pleasures. When we eat in a healthy way, we give ourselves permission to eat and enjoy it. Janice has discussed finding and maintaining a healthy weight without having to give up foods, and by learning to deal with your emotions directly rather than through food. You can learn to relax about the process of eating and still enjoy your favorite foods.

We live in an era in which food is plentiful. We have lots of wonderful, rich food available to us. Sometimes we have trouble getting enough activity for the amount of food we eat, or we eat for emotional reasons, and then we gain weight that makes us uncomfortable. Weight is a balance between the amount of calories that we take in and the amount that we burn each day. Consequently the typical weight loss prescription has been to reduce the calories we take in. This is dieting. Unfortunately, for most people it doesn't work. Our bodies are very well adapted to protect against starvation, and that is what a diet it. There is a way to find and keep a healthy weight. The best solution is learning to enjoy eating, dealing with one's emotions, getting a healthy, balanced diet, and increasing the amount of energy our bodies burn. Janice has thoroughly covered the emotional side of eating. As we go through this material in Appendix I, we will focus on the physical aspects of healthy eating, and help you understand why our bodies fight against dieting, and how to recapture the pleasure of eating in a healthy way.

The first step is learning not to be afraid of food or overeating. Your body can self-regulate how much you eat according to your needs. You just need to listen to and trust your body. Young children do this naturally. We can relearn how to trust our own hunger and appetite needs. When your body is comfortable that you will be fed enough on a regular basis, there will be less of a drive to overeat due to the physical need.

What happens when we diet? Studies of normal weight people placed on reduced calorie diets show that people became obsessed with food. Even when the diet was over and they received their normal level of calories, they were still obsessed with the fear that they wouldn't get enough to eat. When allowed, some of these people ate all day. This is contrary to the common belief that overweight people innately have less willpower and are just self-indulgent. When we are starved (equate this with dieting) our body's protective mechanisms take over. Survival is a powerful instinct. For most of us, dieting is not the way to lose weight in the long run.

When we diet we lose both fat and muscle. The problem is that we don't want to lose muscle. That is where we burn the most energy (calories), so when we lose muscle mass, our metabolism automatically turns down. We burn fewer calories. There is also a mechanism where our body adapts to use calories more efficiently when starved. So our metabolism takes a double hit, using much fewer calories than before dieting. After a diet, people can't eat as much as they did before without regaining more weight than they lost. This doesn't seem fair, but it is all part of the body's defense against starvation. Over the ages, people who could survive periods of famine were genetically preferred. Unfortunately, we still have bodies that are better adapted to protect us against starvation than to deal with abundance.

Dieting studies have showed that when people were allowed to eat at their normal levels after dieting, they tended to regain fat first, even when on a rigorous exercise program. This is also part of the body's protection against starvation. After a diet, the body adapts to store fat preferentially, anticipating that it may be starved again. Fat is nature's way of storing energy; it is concentrated calories. After a diet, our bodies are very good at storing fat – not exactly what we had in mind when we started our first diet.

Therefore, it is in our genes to protect against dieting. If we want to have a healthy weight and feel good about our bodies and our health, we can make healthy choices, choose a wide variety of foods, and enjoy wonderful food. Then we can be patient as our body adapts to healthier eating.

Healthy eating has to do with nurturing your body and your senses. It has to do with trusting yourself and learning to self-regulate how much you eat according to what you need. We eat for many reasons. One component is eating to satisfy our hunger. We also need to satisfy our appetite. This includes how we experience the taste, texture, temperature, small and appearance of the food. Food has a strong emotional component that has to do with being nurtured. If we take care to satisfy these many components of eating, we are more likely to be satisfied with an amount of food that will allow us to keep a healthy weight. You can learn to eat well, relax and enjoy eating.

Some simple tools follow. Mostly they have to do with learning to nurture ourselves. It is important to learn to enjoy eating and to eliminate the fear that you won't get enough to eat or that you won't be allowed to eat food that you enjoy. As Janice said, denial and deprivation lead to binge eating.

INITIALLY, MAKE A POINT OF EATING IN A PLACE THAT IS MEANT FOR EATING. Eating in front of the TV or at the kitchen counter or even standing in front of the refrigerator door probably is going to be unconscious eating. Sit down at a table. Have a tablecloth or pretty place mat under your plate. Yes, use a plate (or bowl or whatever is appropriate). Make eating a pleasurable and self-nurturing time. Providing yourself with a nice setting for eating is just as nurturing to the appetite and to your emotional side as is the food. After you are at a comfortable weight and enjoy a comfortable relationship with food, an occasional meal in front of the TV is okay. Remember, we want to be flexible.

CALM YOURSELF. This could mean anything from

a centering exercise (deep relaxation), saying a blessing or grace, or just taking a few deep breaths and shaking out any tension. This will allow you to focus on the meal.

PAY ATTENTION TO THE PROCESS OF EATING. How many times have you heard yourself say that you ate...a whole cake, a whole bag of cookies, a jumbo bag of potato chips...and you don't even remember eating? This is unconscious eating. If you don't remember the process of eating, you definitely have not satisfied your appetite. Being aware of what we eat is important to the process of feeling fully satisfied with a meal.

It helps to separate the process of eating from the rest of your life. It's easy to overeat if you are reading, watching TV, or working on a project. This is more of that unconscious eating. There will never be enough food if you don't focus in on the event of eating and let all your senses appreciate it.

EAT SLOWLY. When you take your first bite, take time to notice the flavors, the way the food feels in your mouth. Is it hot or cold? Chewy or crunchy? How does it feel going down? Eating is a sensual experience. Sometimes it's fun to eat fast, but most of the time we miss out on the joy if we do it fast – just like sex.

IF THIS IS A MEAL, INCLUDE A VARIETY OF FOODS. Have foods you enjoy. Include a variety of textures and temperatures. The cool crunch of a salad with the clean taste of a vinaigrette dressing is very fresh on the palate. Balance this with a crusty slice of Italian bread. Then have some spicy Arrabiata pasta to wake up your mouth. A glass of red wine refreshes. Finish the classic Italian way with fresh fruits, satisfying your taste for sweets and bringing completion to the meal.

Fruits and vegetables bring bright colors and interesting tastes and textures to liven up our meals. More colors on your plate makes for a more attractive presentation, and as a bonus, you are more likely to get a wide range of nutrients. Fruits and vegetables help to satisfy your body and senses.

EAT UNTIL YOU FEEL FULL. Satisfy yourself. When people are in the habit of dieting, desserts are the "forbidden foods." In fact, desserts are a normal way to provide completion to a meal. They supply different tastes and textures from the rest of our meal. Sweetness can provide a sense of satisfaction and finally quench our appetite. Eating the dessert with the meal will allow you to be satisfied with a smaller amount than if you waited until later. For one thing, after you have just eaten a meal, you are less hungry. Secondly, if you want something sweet after dinner, and don't satisfy that craving, it is going to build up. Then you probably will end up eating more than will make you feel comfortable and you won't feel as good about yourself.

When you know that it is okay to eat until you are satisfied, you will begin to be more aware of the gradations of your feelings of hunger and fullness. Dieters tend to only respond to extremes of fullness and hunger. They are in the habit of not eating unless they feel really hungry. Then they tend not to realize they have had enough until they are over-full.

When you have given yourself permission to eat as much as is needed to satisfy yourself, and you choose foods you enjoy, you can stop when you are comfortably full. If you are afraid that you're never going to get the chance to eat chocolate cake again, you are going to be tempted to eat it all.

Respond to your internal needs, not external demands. You don't have to clean your plate. It's more of a waste to put excess food on your hips than in the trash.

Studies of small children show that children who self-regulate tend to eat the same amount of calories every day, even if some meals are larger and some smaller. Children who are told to clean their plates or taught to eat according to time constraints lose their ability to self-regulate. You want to recapture the ability to eat until you are satisfied, and then stop.

GIVE YOURSELF PERMISSION TO EAT. This takes a lot of pressure off you and helps you conquer the fear of food. This can be difficult if you have friends or relatives who have taken on the role of "food police." External regulation never works. For one thing, it doesn't satisfy you. Most importantly, your goal is to understand and listen to your needs, not someone else's idea of what you need. Get these external voices out of the equation.

Food police can also be your idea of surrogate parents. They may trigger rebellious behavior that will end up causing you to overeat. Relieve them of responsibility. You are the only one responsible for how you eat, and you don't have to answer to anyone.

FEED YOURSELF ON A REGULAR BASIS. We all need at least three meals a day, and most people need one or two snacks. The classic dieting behavior is to skip lunch (or breakfast and lunch), with the idea that this will help you lose weight. It doesn't. It makes you more hungry at the next meal and you end up over compensating. Your body is afraid that it will be starved again, so it drives you to eat as much as you can.

If you feed yourself at relatively regular times, you will start to become more calm about the process of eating. And, food is a fun and pleasurable part of the day.

REMEMBER THAT IT IS NORMAL TO EAT MORE AT SOME TIMES AND LESS AT OTHERS. Listen to your hunger. Listen to your appetite. It is liberating to be able to respond to our own internal clues than to some external idea of how much we should eat. If we are sure that we are going to get enough to eat, the pressure to overeat at times will diminish. We are developing a healthy relationship with food. And as in any relationship, there will be up times and down times. It's all normal. So just relax and appreciate the variations in hunger and appetite.

Many of my clients tell me that they really feel out of control during the week before their periods. Most women take in 500 extra calories each day during this time. They are surprised to learn that this is normal. It is a time for growing new tissue. We need extra calories for growth. The good news is that it goes away. We lose this extra tissue when we menstruate. And yes, we often retain water during this time. Just watch out for excess salt, and remember that the extra weight will go away soon. If you try to fight this natural need for extra calories, it is probably going to
set you up for failure. Don't panic or feel guilty, it's just part of nature.

TRY TO AVOID CONSTANT FOOD CUES WHEN YOU ARE NOT EATING. Avoid having food out on the counter. If you are going to have quick foods available, make some of them healthy foods. Obviously if you have lots of chips around, it's easy to overeat. Healthier choices are fresh fruits and cut up vegetables. It seems like we all have trouble getting enough fruits and vegetables, so using them as munchies can help. If you are concerned that you end up throwing out fresh food that doesn't get eaten, try your local grocery salad bar. This is a great source of cut up fruits and vegetables, where you can pick up just the amount that you are going to eat today or in the next few days. It is a great way to avoid waste, and still have the fresh foods you want. You know what foods you are likely to overeat. Buy these foods individually packaged. This takes away a lot of the temptation to finish the whole cake or gallon of ice cream. Buy smaller containers of ice cream and small, individual servings of chips. Minimizing the calorie-dense foods that you have on hand, or at least increasing the amount of work you need to go to in order to eat them, will make it easier to avoid out-of-control eating.

LOW-FAT FOODS ARE NOT THE ANSWER TO EVERY DIETING DILEMMA. Research has shown that many of us eat larger amounts when we knowingly include low-fat foods in a meal. We lose our sensitivity to our internal cues; we ignore our own sense of hunger and appetite. Besides, many low- or no-fat baked goods have just as many calories as the original food. For example, some of the well known no-fat cookies have just as many calories per cookie as an Oreo! So you might as well choose the one you like most. Other no/low-fat baked goods may taste like cardboard, and again the calories may be the same as the original product. In order for the foods to be satisfying, the taste has to be great. I always tell my clients (and Janice agrees) that if you have a craving for something chocolate-y or sweet, make it the best you can find. And enjoy it! That will allow you to be satisfied with a moderate amount. You won't need to keep eating and eating. Overeating usually doesn't occur because your hunger isn't satisfied, it's your appetite that needs to be pleased or your emotional state.

This leads us to the concept of "good food, bad food." Chronic dieters tend to think about food in terms of whether the food is "guilt-producing" or not.

Initially, as you develop a healthier relationship with food, it is most important to listen to your hunger and appetite cues as you choose what and how much to eat. Include your favorite foods. Later as you become more comfortable with listening to your body and experiencing fullness as being okay, then you can start to consider balancing your nutrient needs. Your first priority is learning to satisfy yourself. You don't need to fear food.

GET REGULAR EXERCISE. Although some people are afraid that exercise will cause them to eat more, the facts are that exercise helps people to self-regulate how much they eat. Remember that our metabolic rate depends on the amount of muscle tissue we have. Exercising helps us maintain or build our muscles. This means we are burning more calories even when we are sitting in front of the television. We all know that aerobic exercise helps us burn extra calories. It also boosts our metabolism for up to a day and a half after exercise. The more we burn, the more we can eat and keep a healthy weight. Be realistic and choose
an exercise plan that is fun and that you can find time for in your life. Remember that dieting lowers the metabolism, and we want to keep it high. Exercise is the dieting antidote.

A BALANCED DIET
Variety is the answer to finding a balanced diet. A healthy diet is based on a foundation of carbohydrate rich foods including grains, breads,

pasta, rice, cereals, fruits and vegetables. We also need protein and foods rich in calcium and iron. When you have a balanced diet, extras like sweets and chips provide interest and don't compromise your nutritional health.

High Protein Diets

People with a history of dieting may be fearful of some types of foods, and feel that they need to restrict them. Generally this means they try to reduce breads and other carbohydrates. Diet trends come and go, and the high protein, low carbohydrate philosophy has recently become trendy again in some circles. The latest rationale is that a high protein diet will be better for someone who is insulin resistant (IR)

IR is a condition in which the body produces enough insulin, but the body's tissues are less responsive to it. This means that blood sugars tend to stay higher than normal, but not so high that the person is considered to have diabetes. IR can generally be controlled by dropping 5-15 pounds and increasing our exercise.

Being overweight tends to be associated with IR, so maybe a high protein diet is the perfect solution for weight loss – right? Wrong!

First, let's look at the effects of a high protein diet. Our body can only use a certain amount of protein. What does it do with the leftovers? It strips off ammonia, turns it into urea, and we get rid of it (in urine). To do this, we need lots of water. So initially we lose water weight.

You may think that weight is weight, so any way you lose is good. Not true. Water weight returns, easily. In addition, all that extra urine puts a load on our kidneys. Back in the '60s and '70s when high protein diets were heavily promoted (even medically supervised), some of these dieters had severe kidney problems including kidney failure.

High meat diets are associated with increased levels of heart disease from the high levels of cholesterol and saturated fats in meats (cholesterol is found in animal-based foods). Heart disease may also be associated with the high levels of iron in meats.

Studies of Japanese men living in the U.S. versus those living in Japan also suggest that high protein diets can increase risk of developing diabetes and insulin resistance – Whoops! Wasn't this the problem it was supposed to solve? High protein diets are not the best way to nurture our body or our health.

Balanced, Healthy Diets

If high protein diets aren't the answer, what is? Balance. Higher amounts of plant-based foods. We know that people with diets rich in plant-based foods have a reduced risk of heart disease, cancer, diabetes, and obesity. A healthy diet is rich in carbohydrates (especially complex carbs), moderate in fats, and provides adequate protein, vitamins and minerals. Moderation of fat helps two ways.

Fats are concentrated calories – more than twice the calories as the same amount of carbs or protein. And, basically, the only thing the body can do with fat is store it as fat.

Where are the risks from eating lots of carbs? Some high carbohydrate foods are overly rich in calories, and poor in other nutrients. For example, many foods with high levels of sugars can be described this way. If they make up the majority of our diet, we may not get enough vitamins and minerals. For people who are insulin-resistant or diabetic, blood sugars can rise.

Please remember that when balanced with other types of foods, sweets still are part of a healthy diet. There are lots of high carb foods that are rich in vitamins, minerals and fiber, and won't send your blood sugar sky high, including whole wheat breads, pasta with vegetable sauce, rice and beans, an orange.

Not everything has to be high fiber; choose the

foods you enjoy. You can balance your diet by adding more vegetables and fresh fruits. They will give the fiber which allows your body to moderate the rate of sugar flowing into the blood as you digest food, and will help to provide fullness.

We do need protein foods, even if we aren't going to make our diet a high protein one. Most Americans tend to get way more than they need. We need 3-5 ounces of protein-rich food per day. When we can, we should choose lower fat meats. Anything with the word "loin" in it will be lower fat. Round and chuck cuts are lean. Skinless white poultry will be low fat. Watch out for some types of ground turkey which are ground with the skin and can be high in fat.

In addition to meats and poultry, seafood is generally low in fat. Steamed, grilled, poached or baked fish can be very low in fat and low in calories.

Balancing Your Diet at Various Calorie Levels							
Approximate serving sizes for food groups to give daily calories (average calories/serving)	1200	1400	1600	1800	2000	2200	2400
grain foods (80): 1 slice bread ½ bun, bagel ½ c pasta ½ c rice ½ c hot cereal 3/4 - 1¼ c cold cereal	6	6	7	8	9	10	11
vegetables (25): ½ c cooked 1 c raw	2	3	4	4	5	5	5
fruits (60): ½ c canned 1 c raw	2	2	2	3	3	3	4
low fat dairy (90): 1 c milk ½ c cottage cheese 1 oz cheese	2	2	3	3	4	4	4
lean meats, fish, poultry (55):1 oz cooked 1 egg	4	4	4	5	5	5	6
sweets (50): 1 T sugar	1	2	2	2	2	2	2
fats (125): 1 T	1	2	2	2	2	3	3

Shellfish are especially low in fat, and are considered to be heart-healthy – not high in cholesterol, as was once thought. Shrimp has only 70 calories per 3 ounce serving compared with 120 calories for 3 ounces of skinless chicken breast. You have a lot of choices for lower fat meats, fish and poultry that will give you a lot of variety in your diet.

If you are a vegetarian, good protein sources include beans, nuts and seeds. These will also supply many of the same vitamins and minerals found in meat. Dairy products are great protein sources, and bread and vegetables will help supply smaller amounts of protein. It is unusual for vegetarians to have diets deficient in protein, but it can happen for picky eaters, vegans, and people who don't like beans. Becoming a vegetarian doesn't just mean eliminating meat from your diet; you also need to have something to replace it. In general, vegetarians will tend to have less of a problem with weight because meat is one of the higher fat foods in our diet. However, vegetarians who eat lots of junk food and high-fat pastries can have high-fat diets and that means high calories.

If you are eating a balanced diet, with lots of plant-based foods, you are probably getting the right amount of vitamins and minerals. Women can have trouble getting enough calcium, and this is very important for avoiding osteoporosis. Getting three glasses of skim milk will provide a good boost of calcium to go along with the calcium we get from some vegetables. Unfortunately many of us have replaced milk with carbonated drinks, which have no calcium. In fact, the phosphoric acid in colas may bind up any calcium we take in, so it is poorly absorbed. Calcium supplements are often recommended if we don't get enough in our diets. However, they may reduce our absorption of zinc which is important for our immune system, wound healing, and sexual function. Generally, the vitamins and minerals we get from a balanced diet are better absorbed if we take supplements. Iron can be another concern for women, especially if little red meat is eaten. Low levels of iron can lead to anemia, which causes lower energy. Beans and dried fruits are good iron sources in a vegetarian diet.

For people who have been on many diets, and are used to worrying about "bad" and "good" foods, it can be difficult to know what is a healthy diet. Following is a chart that will help you put together a healthy diet and get the right amounts of vitamins and nutrients. You can mix or match from this chart, knowing what the various calories are. However, for a good balance of vitamins, minerals and fiber, it will help to stay as close as possible to this guide. To calculate how many calories you need, multiply your weight by 15 for a good approximation. If you want to lose a half to one pound a week (a good, healthy rate), subtract 250-500 calories a day. Do not go below 1200 calories a day, since it is almost impossible to get the right amounts of vitamins and minerals with fewer calories. Also, you don't want to trigger your body's mechanisms that protect against starvation.

Following are some examples of a daily intake of 1400 calories and 1800 calories, to give you a feeling for what can be included and how to incorporate variety, treats, and one snack. If some meals seem big, you could always save part for another snack later in the day.

1400/1800 Calorie Sample Menu Chart

	1400 Calorie diet	1800 Calorie diet
Breakfast	Cheerios - 3/4 cup, with 4 ounces skim milk, and ½ banana, sliced	sesame seed bagel (3½ ")
	whole wheat toast with 1 T strawberry jam	light cream cheese - 1 ounce
	orange juice - 4 ounces	orange juice - 4 ounces
	coffee, black	skim milk - 6 ounces
Lunch	Beef sandwich: 1½ ounces lean beef, sliced, on 2 slices whole wheat bread, with slice light Swiss cheese, 2 slices tomato, lettuce, mustard	Cheeseburger: Quarter pound medium- lean ground beef, American cheese on hamburger bun. Topped with 2 slices tomato, lettuce, mustard & catsup
	pretzels - 15	French fries - 15
	diet cola	tossed salad with 2 T fat free dressing
	chocolate chip cookie	diet cola
		2 Oreos
Afternoon snack	½ cup carrot sticks with 1 oz salsa	3 cups popcorn (air popped)
	iced tea with artificial sweetner	iced tea with artificial sweetner
Dinner	Spaghetti: 1 cup cooked pasta with ½ cup marinara sauce, topped with Parmesan cheese	Baked potato - medium
	broccoli - ½ cup	broiled salmon - 2.5 ounces
	Italian bread - 1 slice	mixed steamed vegetables - ½ cup
	Light praline ice cream - ½ cup	French bread - 1 slice
	water, coffee or diet soda	white wine - 3½ ounces
		banana-strawberry frozen yogurt (Ben & Jerry's) - ½ cup
Analysis	1424 calories, 64% carbohydrate, 18% protein, 18% fat, meets RDA for essential vitamins and minerals, 19 g fiber.	1832 calories, 53% carbohydrate, 18% protein, 26% fat, meets RDA for essential vitamins and minerals, 16 g fiber.

As long as we are encouraging you to eat lots of fruits and vegetables, you may want to know about the added benefits. Studies of people who eat high amounts of plant foods show that they have lower rates of some cancers, heart disease, and diabetes.

The cancer protection factor is especially exciting. Plants actually make chemicals which protect them from bacteria, viruses, and from the elements. These chemicals can also protect us. For example, men who eat 10 or more servings of tomatoes a week have a 54% lower risk of developing prostate cancer.

The vegetables in the broccoli family are also high in protective factors. Most fruits and vegetables contain some of these beneficial compounds. The high fiber in fruits, vegetables, and whole grains protect against colon cancer. Some of these fibers also help to reduce cholesterol and reduce risk of gall bladder disease.

In the media we hear a lot about food that is "bad" for us, but it's also reassuring to know that food can protect us. We encourage healthy choices, filled with all types of foods, foods that you love.

Some of the most significant steps that we can take to enhance our health are to increase the variety in our diets by increasing the fruits, vegetables, and grains in our diet. It makes it easier to achieve a healthy weight, avoid health problems, and still have room for your favorite foods.

The keys to achieving a healthy weight that we can maintain are:

- balancing what we eat with our activity;
- enjoying variety and flexibility in what we eat; and
- keeping in touch with our feelings, dealing with them directly.

Relax and enjoy great eating!

Marla Heller, R.D., L.D.
Transitions Nutrition Consulting

Suggested Readings

Following are lists of books (by category) I have found to be excellent resources. There are many more choices, so feel free to browse in your local bookstore and see what might "feel right" for you.

WEIGHT-RELATED RESOURCES

- Bruch, Hilde, M.D. *The Golden Cage.* Random House, 1979.

- Chernin, Kim. *The Hungry Self: Women, Eating and Identity.* Harper Collins, 1996.

- Chernin, Kim. *The Obsession: Reflections on the Tyranny of Slenderness.* Harper Collins, 1994.

- Cohen, Mary Anne. *French Toast for Breakfast: Declaring Peace with Emotional Eating.* Gurze Books, 1995.

- Hall, Lindsey and Cohn, Leigh. *Bulimia: A Guide to Recovery.* Gurze Books, 1992.

- Hirshmann, Jane and Hunter, Carol. *Overcoming Overeating.* Fawcett Books, 1989.

- Kano, Susan. *Making Peace with Food.* Harper Collins, 1989.

- Katherine, Anne, M.A., *Anatomy of a Food Addiction.* Gurze Books, 1996.

- Latimer, Jane Evans. *Beyond the Food Game: A Spiritual and Psychological Approach to Healing Emotional Eating.* Living Quest, 1993.

- Latimer, Jane Evans. *Living Binge-Free.* Living Quest, 1991.

- Miller, Caroline. *My Name Is Caroline.* Gurze Books, 1991.

- O'Neill, Cherry Boone. *Dear Cherry: Questions and Answers on Eating Disorders.* Crossroad Press, 1987.

- O'Neill, Cherry Boone. *Starving for Attention.* Hazelden, 1995.

- Orbach, Susie. *Fat Is a Feminist Issue.* Berkley Publications, 1994.

- Ray, Sondra. *The Only Diet There Is.* Celestial Arts, 1995.

- Roth, Geneen. *Appetites.* NAL-Dutton, 1997.

- Roth, Geneen. *Breaking Free from Compulsive Eating.* NAL-Dutton, 1993.

- Roth, Geneen. *Feeding the Hungry Heart.* NAL-Dutton, 1993.

- Roth, Geneen. *Why Weight? A Guide to Ending Compulsive Eating.* NAL-Dutton, 1989.

- Sandbek, Terrence, Ph.D. *The Deadly Diet: Recovering from Anorexia and Bulimia.* New Harbinger, 1993.

- Siegel, Michele, Ph.D., Brisman, Judith, Ph.D., and Weinshel, Margot, MSW. *Surviving an Eating Disorder.* Harper Collins, 1989.

- Zerbe, Kathryn J. *Women Betrayed: Eating Disorders and Treatments.* Gurze Books, 1995.

BODY IMAGE

- Hutchinson, Marcia Germaine, Ed.D. *Transforming Body Image.* Crossing Press, 1985.

- Newman, Leslea. *SomeBody to Love: A Guide to Loving the Body You Have.* Third Side Press, 1991.

- Rodin, Judith, Dr. *Body Traps.* Morrow, 1993.

RELAXATION/MEDITATION

- Benson, Herbert, M.D. and Klipper, Miriam. *Begin the Relaxation Response.* Avon Books, 1976.

- Carrington, Patricia, Ph.D. *Freedom in Meditation.* Pace Education Systems, 1977.

- Colby, Anne. *Daily Meditations for Dieters.* Carol Publications Group, 1994.

- Goliszek, Andrew. *Breaking the Stress Habit.* Caroline Press, 1987.

- Breathnach, Sarah Ban. *The Simple Abundance Journal of Gratitude.* Warner Books, 1996.

- Gawain, Shakti. *Creative Visualization.* New World Library, 1995.

- Gawain, Shakti. *Living in the Light.* Bantam Books, 1993.

- Gawain, Shakti. *The Path to Transformation.* Nataraj, 1993.

- Johnson, Debbie. *Think Yourself Thin.* Hyperion, 1996.

- Morgan, Marlo. *Mutant Messages Down Under.* Harper Collins, 1995.

- Redfield, James. *The Celestine Prophecy.* Warner Books, 1994.

- Weiss, Brian, M.D., *Many Lives, Many Masters.* Warner Books, 1996.

- Weiss, Brian, M.D., *Only Love Is Real.* Warner Books, 1996.

- Williamson, Marianne. *A Return to Love.* Harper Collins, 1996.

- Williamson, Marianne. *A Woman's Worth.* Ballantine Books, 1994.

- Zukav, Gary. *The Seat of the Soul.* Simon & Schuster, 1990.

- Burns, David. D., M.D. *Feeling Good: The New Mood Therapy.* Avon Books, 1992.

- Buscaglia, Leo. Living, Loving and Learning. Slack, Inc., 1982.

- Lerner, Harriet, Ph.D. *Dance of Anger.* Harper Collins, 1989.

- Lerner, Harriet, Ph.D. *Dance of Intimacy.* Harper Collins, 1990.

- Peck, Scott M. *The Road Less Travelled.* Simon Schuster, 1993.

- Pipher, Mary, Ph.D. *Reviving Ophelia.* Ballantine Books, 1995.

- Sheehey, Gail. *Pathfinders.* Bantam, 1982.

To Order Copies of
I Always Start My Diet on Monday

Name . . . .

Mailing Address . . . .

Phone/Fax . . . .

VISA/MasterCard # (Circle One) . . . .

Expiration Date . . . .

    Please send (   ) copies @$13.95 . . . .
    Illinois residents add 7.5% tax . . . .
    Add shipping/handling fees
        $2.50 for one book . . . .
        $3.50 for two books . . . .
        $4.25 for three books . . . .

TOTAL . . . .

Phone 847.441.5470 to order by phone.
Fax 847.446.8618 to order by Fax.

OR:
Mail this form with check, money order or VISA/MasterCard number to:

Pearl Publishing
540 Frontage Road, Suite 2045
Northfield, Illinois 60093